Embracing the Battle

Secrets of Victory
From a Warrior Mom

Laura Kasbar

Printed in the United States of America

First Printing, 2018

ISBN 978-1-7322143-1-6

Gemiini Systems
157 S. Howard Street Suite 601
Spokane WA 99201

www.gemiini.org

This book is dedicated to all of the parents who keep the faith and fight love's battle despite waiting for years to hear their child's voice. You are the real heroes of the story. And to the greatest warrior mother of all time, the Mother of God.

Who is she that cometh forth as the morning rising, fair as the moon, bright as the sun, ***terrible as an army set in array?***

- Canticle of Canticles 6:10

Foreword

I just finished reading this book, and I don't think I've ever been as captivated by a story as I have by this one. Embracing the Battle reads like a best-selling novel and I couldn't put it down. When Laura Kasbar first asked me to consider writing this foreword, I was hesitant mainly because my schedule was currently over-full! I just didn't have the time to try to read and digest a book, then write a foreword – and she was asking for it in ONE WEEK! But, as you'll see in the pages to come, Laura has that quality that every child with special needs should have in a parent: She believes that any problem WILL have a solution, and she won't stop at anything until that solution is implemented.

I'm not sure how you got me to carve out a few extra hours in one of my office's busiest weeks in the middle of flu season, with my own book deadline approaching, all the while launching a new radio show. The same way you didn't take no for an answer when trying to find help for your own children and have eventually gone on to help thousands of other children with what you created. You are a mom on a mission!

I've always said that when a child is diagnosed with a poorly understood disorder (like autism), we usually see that parent become an expert in that particular disorder and will quickly learn more than the child's own general doctors. Laura Kasbar took this concept and turned the dial up to ELEVEN!

I want everyone to read this book! Pediatricians, therapists and anyone else that is on the front lines of screening for autism as well as any parent with concerns about their child's development. There are dozens of books written by mothers who have fought this battle, but Embracing the Battle offers solutions.

As a pediatrician I thought I knew about every available therapy for kids with special needs... I didn't. I wondered, "Am I the only one that doesn't know about this?" Why doesn't everyone know about this, AND USE IT?! I even asked one of my colleagues, who is a local expert in biomedical treatments for autism. The limit of his knowledge on Gemiini was, "I think one of my patients uses it and likes it" and that was it.

About an hour into reading, I put the book down and immediately called three of my patients and one of my family members and told them to start the Gemiini program with their kids. These kids ranged from a two-year-old that was just diagnosed with autism last week, to a 28-year-old with Down syndrome that has had just about every therapy available – except for this one. The book goes on to cite a substantial amount of positive clinical evidence for Gemiini's Discrete Video Modeling. This helps me recommend this therapy without hesitation.

Thank you for asking me to write this foreword, as I would have never read this book otherwise: I'm just too busy. I would have missed out on this amazing information. This will help so many of my patients! Gemiini's Ten Signs of Autism screening tool is now given to all my parents of toddlers, and it is making my job a lot easier!

Dr. Jim Sears, Pediatrician

Contents

Introduction

The day before publication I received last minute review edits from a person whose literary advice I highly esteem. She told me that I had too many irrelevant details which, although interesting, aren't necessary to the story. She also said that in some places it was a bit too personal.

I want to tell the reader that I know all of this.

I know that I wrote this book from a very personal place.

I know that I have added details that seem irrelevant to the story.

I know that it is a departure from other books on this subject.

I did this because I want you to know me, and to know that I am not Superwoman. My children are not one-in-a-billion savants. I make mistakes. I fail.

The grace of God alone has saved me from falling on my face. (Oh, and I also know that "you're not supposed to talk about God.")

The writing may be amateurish, but it is genuine. I ask you all to reserve judgement (on anything) until the end of the book as things tend to take a dramatic turn as time goes on. My goal is not to win a Pulitzer Prize (which is well beyond my ability anyway). I wrote this book because I want you to know what is possible, and to demonstrate how old-fashioned ingenuity can and needs to permeate our everyday life. I want to warn you to not let your failures deprive you of your successes.

A path to happiness can always be found, even if the destination changes half way through the journey.

And who's to say that your new destination won't be one thousand times more beautiful than the place you thought you were going?

PART I

Chapter 1:
Surfing Saved My Life

My first memory is of myself, alone on a surfboard, and I know I am going to die.

I am two years old. I have been swimming since the age of ten months, and surfing with my father for about that long, so I'm not afraid of water. However, this time is different.

My dad lets go.

I am lying on the board, and when the (very small) wave comes, he lets go. I don't know letting go was his intention. I don't even know he has let go until I hear his voice get further and further away.

I am looking at the shore in the distance and know I will never make it there. I scream over and over, "Save me! Save me! Save me!"

But—I don't die. I don't get hurt. I do yell at my dad, with a toddler's pronunciation, "Why did you wet go! I aahmost died!" But after about five minutes, I want to go out again. And this time I tell him, "Wet me do it mysewf!"

Thirty minutes later, I am having the time of my life.

* * *

Fast-forward seven years. I am nine years old and body surfing, when out of the blue a colossal set comes in. I stare up at this immense wall of water, which must be twenty feet high. Inhaling so deeply I think my lungs will explode, I dive down to the bottom of the sea floor, dig my fingers into the sand, and hold on for dear life. I know I must wait until the wave is well past me, or it will just rip me out of the water and propel me over the falls, back into the churning surf. If I panic, I'll run out of air too soon. So, my only choice is to remain as calm as possible and wait.

It feels like an eternity.

All I can think is, "I am not going to die here."

I make it back to the surface and gasp for air, only to see another wall of water approaching like a giant, foaming dragon. Once more I suck in as much air as I can, dive down, and hold onto the sand. This repeats four or five times. The last time I come up, I see a lifeguard paddling toward me, yelling at me to come with him.

After the first wave, I might have gone willingly. But by the fourth, I have become a wave slayer, and I am sure there are more dragons approaching. I retort, "Go away! Leave me alone! I'm fine." In the end, I am forced to retreat, but I just move down the beach and re-engage the battle outside of the life guard's view.

Decades have passed, but what I learned has not. Surfing taught me to face my fears—to think fast, and to never say die. It taught me that sometimes "scary" is just the beginning of fun, and that there is no better feeling in the world than "I did it!" The decidedly American (and sometimes naïve) conviction that I truly can do anything, overcome any obstacle, and be the better for having done it has carried me through the trials of life better than anything else I have ever learned.

It is what got me through the second-scariest day of my life—the day my twins were diagnosed with autism.

* * *

While I am in the hospital giving birth to my sixth child, a family member takes my three-year-old twins, Lucy and John, to a local school to be evaluated. They aren't talking yet, but—to be honest—I'm not concerned. They are twins, and everyone knows that twins are late talkers. My husband, Brian, didn't speak in sentences until he was four. We have a bilingual household. All these things give me ample excuse to be complacent.

Four days later, my husband and I walk into a conference room at the school. Six or seven people sit at one end of a large wooden table, waiting for us. All have the sort of grave expression one sees at a funeral for someone who died suddenly or took his own life. I am confused, as I expect to talk to just one teacher and have her tell me, "The twins are fine. They will talk when they are ready."

That's not what this group is saying.

Each professional lists the assessments she had administered and then describes the results. Each time, the twins score below a one-year-old age equivalent.

I sit there, frozen, holding my four-day-old newborn. I don't know where this all is going, but I know that these people in front of me are very, very concerned. They ask me pointed questions about the twins, and about John in particular. They seem to know both children well.

"Does John like to stack blocks really high?"

"Does he line up all of his toys, or anything he can get his hands on?"

"Does Lucy understand when you say, 'Go get me a (fill in the blank)'?"

Like more foaming dragons, the questions kept coming, one after another, after another. The professionals clearly have a reason for asking them, but they aren't letting on what it is. We are so oblivious to the signs of autism that these obvious traits don't send any sort of alarm. We are 100 percent clueless. Finally, my husband speaks up: "Are these things indicative of anything specific?"

When Brian and I fail to catch any of their not-so-subtle hints, a teacher finally says the one thing that will change our lives—and the lives of hundreds of thousands of people around the world.

"We believe that the twins show signs of autism."

She says it in an almost hushed tone, but these words ring out like explosions. They blow apart the future I have envisioned not only for the twins, but for my husband and me. They torpedo every aspect of what I thought my life was about. These words leave a gaping hole in my chest that makes breathing difficult and thinking impossible. The teachers say something about, "preparing for the future," and "non-verbal," but to be honest, to this day I don't remember much after I heard the word "autism."

I leave the building in a silent, numb, state of shock. My feet are moving, but my mind is still back in that conference room, looking into twelve eyes full of pity. As I emerge from this dreamlike state into the sudden reality into which I have been thrust, tears start to roll down my cheeks, and my sobbing grows louder.

I retreat to that toddler-on-the-surfboard. Inside, I am silently screaming, "Save me! Save me! Save me!" But this time, there is no shore in sight. There is just an open horizon, and I am headed out to sea.

Chapter 2:
What A Difference A Day Makes

Inscrutably, Brian seemed to be unfazed by what we'd just heard. He was even confused about why I was crying.

I looked at my husband with an expression of disbelief and blurted out between sobs, "John!"

"What?" Brian said. "It just means that John is going to be like your grandfather."

I didn't know what he was thinking. I sincerely wondered if he had been in the same room with me. My grandfather had been the lead geologist for ARCO, the oil giant. He was one of the most famous people in the field of petroleum development in the world. He had a PhD. He was most definitely not nonverbal autistic.

I said, "What? My grandfather?"

Brian went on, as if it were obvious, "Yeah, you know. He was kind of quiet and spent so much time alone in research."

I came to learn that this was a common reaction of fathers. Denial, avoidance, and deflection can grip dads like a bulldog, along with any other coping mechanism that lets them preserve their vision for the future of their child. Brian instantly created an alternate reality in which the most positive (and least likely) outcome was inevitable. He was violently shaken from his fantasy when I bawled, "John is autistic! They just said he will never speak—that he may spend his life in an institution! My grandfather was a scientist. The two aren't even close!"

To my husband's credit, my words and reaction shook him out of his denial as swiftly as it had set in. He didn't get angry at me or retreat into a silent tantrum, like so many dads do. Instead, he went home and went straight to work on a solution.

* * *

Within twenty-four hours, Brian had devoured just about everything he could find on autism research. He also read everything he could on the legal obligations of different institutions from the school, our home state of Washington, and the federal government.

Back in 2000, there wasn't a lot of information online about autism research. In fact, the only bright spot we could find was a UCLA study by O. Ivar Lovaas, published in 1987, about a type of one-to-one therapy called Applied Behavior Analysis (ABA). The research was conducted over a three-year period and found that 40 percent of children who were exposed to ABA at least forty hours per week became indistinguishable from their typical peers. All the children who were successful in the program started this therapy before they were forty months old.

The twins were thirty-nine months.

A combination of relief and panic took hold of us. We had hope, but we didn't have time.

We found out that a full-time ABA program cost over one hundred thousand dollars per year, each child. And, there were no "BCBAs," or board-certified behavior analysts—the specialists who are trained in this sort of therapy—where we lived in Spokane, Washington.

Brian found that a law passed by the federal government entitled IDEA seemed to demand that the school district cover this therapy. Exactly forty-eight hours after we had been given the life-altering news, we marched back to the same school with a large binder filled with research and legal precedent.

To say that the principal was not at all pleased would be an understatement of gargantuan proportions. I don't think that he had ever been challenged before. In stark contrast, however, the therapists and teachers who I would come to love and admire over the following years were our hidden cheerleaders. They secretly gave us thumbs up and mouthed "Go for it!" as we walked by.

One teacher pulled us aside and whispered, "Your children are going to be fine."

I said, "But just two days ago, you said John would likely be nonverbal his whole life."

"I have been in special education for over twenty years," she said. "I've seen enough kids to know that the children who do well have one thing in common. They have fighters for parents." She looked me in the eye. "Your kids will be just fine."

But, the principal had an ace up his sleeve that we didn't anticipate. This particular school was contracted by our own district to deliver early intervention, as we lived in the smallest school district in the state. Our district had just one school: kindergarten to sixth grade. The principal of the contract school said that he was not obliged to accept the contract and, if we sued for a full ABA program, that he would just cancel the contract with our own district.

I knew that our tiny district's budget wouldn't cover this, and that even if we sued and won, there was just no way to fund it.

And, time was ticking by.

Chapter 3:
"Charge!"

As I lay on my bed, cuddling my newborn, I sensed that great, foaming dragon barreling down on us. This massive wall of destruction was now not a wall of water, but a list of seemingly insurmountable circumstances that wanted to destroy my children. I ticked them off in my mind:

- School district without any resources
- Insurance didn't cover autism therapy
- $200k/per year minimum for therapy
- No BCBAs for hundreds of miles
- Twins had less than 30 days to start therapy
- 6 children, 3 of whom I homeschooled, 1 a newborn
- A demanding construction business that took 10 hours a day of my time
- A massive mortgage

Over the next few days, I could feel my heart skip beats. I had memory lapses for long stretches of time, and my short-term recall was just gone. Several times a day I couldn't remember why I'd walked into a room. I couldn't even remember my older children's names and kept calling everyone "John" or "Lucy." I found out later that these were classic signs of a nervous breakdown, but I didn't have the luxury of relaxing or resting. The less I did, the more quickly I felt the seconds tick by.

That night, my grief awoke me again, as it had done every night since I felt the word AUTISM had impaled my life. I made my way downstairs and noticed a particularly beautiful quality of light shining on the picture of the Holy Face of Jesus that was in the center of the mantel. It was a depiction of the Veronica, the cloth used to wipe Our Lord's face during the Carrying of the Cross, which still holds His image in blood. The face seemed almost living, and I felt compelled by some interior calling to approach it and kneel there in the soft starlight.

For the first time, I felt true empathy for that face. Its expression was one of sacrifice and love. It was sad beyond measure, but willingly suffered. It was entirely selfless. I drew a sort of tortured consolation from knowing that the Man behind the face had sacrificed everything with great purpose.

As I gazed into His eyes, my own filled with tears. I made the most difficult proclamation I have ever uttered, and most likely ever will again. "Dear Lord," I said, "I thank Thee for this cross," and collapsed in a sobbing heap on the floor.

* * *

That night was a turning point. What happened over the next twenty days was nothing short of a series of miracles.

I called anyone and everywhere I could think of to seek help. Somewhere in all the contact information for support groups, university professors, and school therapists, was a woman's name, Corey Valley. Corey had gone to Colorado to train in Applied Behavior Analysis, to work as a personal therapist to another local set of twins with autism. She was the closest thing to a BCBA we had in the entire county.

Corey was available for a few hours per week, at over $150 per hour. She came to my home and started to train me in ABA, and she also referred Kaisa, one of her students, who would be available to work with the twins full time starting in a month. I didn't know how I was going to pay for all of this, but I decided we would cross that bridge when we came to it. We were running recklessly toward a financial cliff, hoping a bridge would be built before we went over the edge.

Waiting for another month to pass was not possible. As my twins' fortieth month mark approached, I embarked on the closest thing to juggling I have ever done. But, instead of balls or bowling pins, I was juggling babies, telephones, and "Barney" action figures.

I sat on a chair with a pillow on my lap to support my nursing baby. Two high chairs were strategically placed in front of me. They held the twins and an assortment of items on their trays. The telephone was placed on a side table within reach, so I could conduct business between therapy sessions. This went on for hours each day, until the twins simply couldn't sit one minute longer. As soon as they were freed, I was back on the phone, quite literally until the battery went dead and I had to switch to a different one.

During those daily juggling routines, Lucy started to become interested in the objects on the trays. She even started to say, "EEEhhhherrr," and raise her arm to make the elephant sound. EEEhhhherrr was her first "word," and that is what she called elephants for quite some time. Once she grasped this first word, the lights were turned on in her little brain. She looked at Brian and me with intent. She knew objects had names. She was trying to communicate with us!

John, however, was decidedly uninterested in what I was doing and spent the entire time in his high chair playing with his fingers and making repetitive noises. He would need more than I knew how to do right now.

* * *

We were able to get the twins in to see a clinical psychologist in less than two weeks. This would be unheard of today, as the wait for a diagnosis can be months, and without one, access to resources is limited. We took the official diagnosis to the Department of Developmental Disabilities (DDD), where we were relieved to learn of a waiver program in place that allowed children with an autism diagnosis to be included in Medicaid, regardless of their parents' income.

This waiver had a window that was open for less than a month—and we made it by just a few days. As far as I know, that waiver didn't open again for over five years.

I cannot overstate how crucial Medicaid was to the future of my children. Private insurance didn't cover autism therapy, and most relevant to our plan of attack, it didn't cover respite hours.

The Medicaid waiver was created to give families at risk for institutionalization a break from the constant stress of caregiving. The idea is that if the state provides respite, families have a greater chance of staying together and the state will save billions in costly institution fees. Under the waiver, Lucy and John were allotted hundreds of hours of respite care per year. I placed an ad with the local university's special education and psychology programs and hired students for respite. In reality, we didn't use them for respite at all. These students were trained in ABA, and they became the foundation of our forty-hour-a-week program.

I must admit that I was breaking the rules here. DDD had strict guidelines against training respite workers in therapy. I, of course, ignored this completely.

I am pretty sure that this rule persists today, to the detriment of all involved. Training respite caregivers in the principles of play-based therapy is nothing more than good sense and plain responsibility. If these people are supposed to work with children who have special needs, they should know how to work with special-needs children! With the crisis in therapy that the United States faces, respite workers are the obvious and only answer. If well trained—even via video training—they can change the futures of millions of people across the country, as they changed my children's lives.

Even with the respite time, we fell short of forty hours of one-to-one therapy for each child. So, Brian and I went to the little school at the end of the road with a plan. At first, the man who served as superintendent/principal/janitor was worried.

He had heard of our demands at the contract school and was just waiting for us to come through his door next.

When we sat down, he didn't even give us a chance to speak. He said, "I know what you want, and you can probably get it if you sue. But, we would have to shut down every after-school program, every extra-curricular activity, and every sports program to cover just your two kids."

"We don't want that," I assured him. "We have a solution that won't cost much. In fact, you probably won't even feel it."

He sat back, pleasantly surprised. This changed everything. He said, "I will do whatever is in my power to help your kids. I'm all ears."

I told him that the Federal Work-Study program would cover most of the university students' pay if they were contracted through the school. I would do all the work to hire and train the students; he just had to sign their monthly checks. I would need about forty hours per week, and the school for their part, would have to pay three dollars per hour.

His eyes opened wide, even wider than the smile on his face, and he replied,

"I'll do it. But I will have to annex your home as part of the school."

Within two months, we had a fully functioning ABA program taking place in our basement: forty-five hours per week, for each child. I could breathe at last, but little did I know the battle was only beginning.

Chapter 4:
I Am Not Going To Die Here

Looking back on those first days of therapy, I have to laugh. We had grown so accustomed to the Addams Family antics that were our family that we didn't even notice how, well, interesting we were. Only years later, when the therapists had become our trusted friends, did they open up to how shocked and confused they were their first week.

The first day that Krista came to interview, Lucy was screaming and rolling from one side of the dining room to the other. She was so loud that it almost defied physics. How these supersonic sound waves could emanate from this tiny, precious little princess was mystifying. Unfortunately, this was a thrice-daily occurrence, and after years of trying, without success, to figure out what was causing her so much anguish, we all just carried on.

John, on the contrary, was nicknamed "The Silent Terror." He would go quietly from room to room messing with everything he could get his hands on. Every morning at five, John would wake up, walk downstairs, and push all the huge dining room chairs in a row. The sound they made scraping on the wooden floor would awaken me, and I'd peek over the upstairs balcony to watch the morning marvel. This tiny boy would put all his weight behind a chair and push it until he had circumvented the table and lined each one up on the right side. He would then sight down the chairs to make sure they were perfectly aligned, walking back and forth to each chair and pushing or pulling it ever so slightly, until he was satisfied.

His next job was to descend the basement steps to the closet under the stairs, where he would remove the two hundred plus stuffed animals amassed by six children under the age of eleven. Carrying them one at a time, starting with the largest, he would climb back up the stairs and place one on each stair. As he came to the bottom and ran out of steps, he would ring them around the entire family room. When all the animals had been placed, he would begin rearranging them from tallest to smallest. The entire exercise—from dining chairs to animals—took hours, and John kept busy for most of the morning each day.

On her first day, Krista passed Lucy, who was screaming and rolling, and then went downstairs past John, who was silently placing his animals on each step. Krista later told me that she was seriously intimidated by the entire spectacle, as she had never had any experience with autism previously. But the sheer absurdity of it all, along with my rather nonplussed attitude, won her over. We added several more wonders of patience and kindness masquerading as college students to the roster as time went by.

With the team assembled, our home became a fully operational clinic, open for business from eight A.M. to six

P.M., Monday through Saturday—and I was the administrator. I spent hours combing through thrift stores to find picture books to cut up into flashcards. I directed the curriculum and created the weekly target choices (and no, we weren't shooting! "Targets" are what they call the individual items to be learned.) The school sent over an SLP (speech pathologist), OT (occupational therapist), and PT (physical therapist), who all trained me as well.

We trained the respite and work-study students in ABA (and yes, I do know that this industry has more acronyms than the space program.) Like any clinic, weekly staff meetings allowed us to brainstorm on how to push the twins to their next level of development and invent tactics to achieve goals faster.

After a few weeks, Lucy Marie Kasbar was TALKING! She was as stubborn as she could be, but she was talking, so that was all that mattered. At first it was just a word or two. She called everyone "Daddy"—even strangers at the grocery store, much to my great embarrassment. She called all animals by the sound they made, and she called all food "pizza."

Although her language was improving, eye contact was still not there. And, while she exhibited some autistic stereotypes, like obsessively carrying around random objects all day, she was waking up to our world more and more each week.

The ABA was working!

* * *

John, on the other hand, was still locked inside his own head. Apart from acknowledging his twin sister, he didn't seem to notice the rest of the family at all. Looking back, that is one of the reasons I hadn't considered that he might have autism. When he played with Lucy, he would look right into her eyes. They would hold hands and laugh together. They had their own language. They were silly together.

It is important for parents to understand that every child does not exhibit the same symptoms of autism in the same way; in fact, certain people may never display some of the symptoms. For some, eye contact—for example—can be present when interacting with parents, but missing with strangers. Children can sometimes show a high interest in playing with others, but other times, be completely uninterested.

After months and months of one-to-one therapy, forty-five hours per week, John still did not understand one single word. We thought maybe he wasn't motivated to learn by the little rewards we had prepared. We got so desperate that we put the therapy table next to the front door because all John wanted was to go outside. This just made him more frustrated. During receptive testing (testing his comprehension), he understood that he was supposed to pick up an object from the table and hand it to us, but he wasn't catching on to which one we wanted. He would just pick up anything in reach and chuck it at the therapist, and then lunge for the door to get out.

He cried. I cried. It was all so heartbreaking.

My mind went back to that school boardroom, where we first heard the news. John may never speak, they said. I didn't believe it then. I couldn't believe it. But, after John spent hundreds of hours trying to learn the word "cup," I realized that maybe they were right. After all, Lucy was talking now. In fact, she was talking quite a bit.

I felt that familiar sensation of lying on the ocean floor with my fingers gripping the sand as the waves raged above me. I will not panic, I told myself. I am not going to die here, and neither is John. I didn't have a solution, but I wasn't going to give up until I did. Or maybe I would die trying?

About this time, Corey Valley came over to the house for a supervisor meeting. I was begging her for some insight on what John's future might hold. She casually said, "Oh, don't worry, Laura. I have been working with a little boy for two years, and he finally said his first word."

That didn't help. In fact, I think that freaked me out even more. A line graph was immediately created in my head. One word every two years wasn't going to get us were we needed to go! Desperate times called for creative measures.

It was later that night that I noticed something extraordinary. As I was coming out of the therapy room, I saw John sitting on the couch with his four siblings, watching a video on television. I remember it was an animated dinosaur film, and he was laughing and hiding his face from the scary T-Rex. I saw that he was engaged with the video more than he ever had been with real life. Then I thought about myself. I had attended university in France and learned French as an adult. I would never have been able to learn the language if I couldn't see the teacher's mouth move. Seeing a person's mouth articulate the words somehow solidified the auditory input I was receiving.

I recalled that I'd had a hard time speaking on the phone in French, or Spanish for that matter, because I needed the visual. Seeing the speaker's face was also essential because I have poor hearing. I thought about John and his learning. He never looked at us. He didn't look at his therapists. How could he learn anything at all that way?

John interacted with the TV. He would look at the TV. I decided I had to get my mouth on the TV.

The next day, I had Brian film a close-up of my face saying "cup" as I held up a cup and filmed many different types of cups for generalization. We filmed me saying "Barney" as I held up a toy (at that time Barney was incredibly motivating). We showed the video to John and Lucy three times that day while they ate in their high chairs. They saw it about ten times altogether.

That night, when I held up the cup, John said, "puc."

The English language does not contain words that describe the rush of emotion I felt at hearing "puc." I didn't even notice that he said it backwards. I just knew now that John would talk. Instantly, the burden of one thousand tons, the chronic sadness that I had carried around for months, had disappeared.

Chapter 5:
The New Normal

Those first six months of therapy were the most taxing of my life. Between the older kids, the newborn, the business, and running a fully operational autism clinic, my brain was pushed to its limit. A word of wisdom to parents of newly diagnosed kiddos: it gets easier.

Once systems were created and we had adopted a new set of habits, the whole clinic started to almost run itself. It was about this time that I read Karyn Seroussi's book Unraveling the Mystery of Autism and Pervasive Development Disorder. The story in this book had a greater effect on my children's therapeutic outcomes than any other single thing we did, and I suggest that every parent of a child on the spectrum read it.

Sixty years ago, autism was thought to be childhood schizophrenia, and 100 percent neurological. We now know that it is every bit as much biological and metabolic as neurological, and that most children with autism suffer from intestinal and digestive problems. Seroussi wrote about her eighteen-month-old boy, newly diagnosed on the autism spectrum, who had red, scaly cheeks and was very thin. He was terribly constipated and ate only wheat- or dairy-based foods. She wrote how removing gluten (wheat protein) and casein (dairy protein) from her son's diet completely changed his health—to the point that, by the time he was in kindergarten, he was indistinguishable from any typically developing child. The evidence she presents is compelling. And the similarities between her son and John were striking.

Looking back, there were signs of autism that we missed in the twins almost since birth, especially with John. He would cry inconsolably for hours and hours each night, for example. Just trying to get enough sleep for the first six months of his life was a full-time job. He was obviously in pain, but no amount of rocking, cuddling, feeding, or changing helped.

Until the twins were about twenty months old, I slept with one on each side of me, so that I could nurse them during the night. Like any typical child, Lucy would snuggle into me when she was finished nursing. John, however, would pull away and roll over as far as he could get. I was worried that he would roll right off the bed, so he had to sleep in the middle between my husband and me. John never wanted to be cuddled, never sought attention or comfort if he was hurt, and didn't seem to notice that we even existed, unless he wanted something. When he did want something, he would grab our hands and pull us toward his desired object, so we could retrieve it for him.

When the twins weaned, I gave them milk in their bottles, and they started to eat more solid food. John was absolutely addicted to milk and would only eat dairy or bread products. He became very thin, his nose ran all the time, and his cheeks were red and chapped. Both twins had gritty, sandy stools in their diapers. I didn't know it at the time, but all of these were markers for allergies and food intolerances and were common with autism.

* * *

John was losing weight no matter how much he ate. At thirty months, he was diagnosed with "failure to thrive." As his weight decreased, so did his interest in anything outside of his inner world. After reading stories about autism and diet online, we had cut back on wheat and dairy. But Seroussi's book inspired me to go completely gluten and casein free. It was the most important decision I made considering the twins, and would change the course of their lives.

We installed a gate on the kitchen and locked all the cupboards and refrigerator. Nothing with even a trace of gluten or casein was allowed within the children's reach. It was hard, at first, as their entire diet had consisted of the very things we were restricting. But in the end, "tough love" prevailed.

During the switch, John refused to eat any protein-based food at all, so I had to get very creative. I boiled chicken and cut it up in tiny pieces to mimic the shape of rice and mixed the two together. As the months went by, the chicken pieces got bigger and bigger, until he would tolerate them. (In an odd coincidence, Temple Grandin would later tell me that they used the same technique to change cattle's diet!) John's dairy milk was replaced with rice milk, and by the grace of Almighty God, he would eat broccoli. He had loved anything to do with wheat bread, but he wasn't having any of the gluten-free bread. I didn't blame him. Back in 2000, rice-flour bread tasted more like cardboard than bread. It is much improved now.

Out of pure desperation to get nutrients into him, I created my own "vitamin bars" with these ingredients:

- Brown rice flour
- Pureed kale
- Ground flax seeds
- Safflower oil
- Baking powder
- Baking soda
- Egg whites
- Salt
- Maple syrup
- Rice milk

He was so addicted to and craving bread that he ate it! And he ate it at every meal. Rice, chicken, broccoli, egg whites, safflower or olive oil, vitamin bread, and melon were all he would eat for two years or longer. And, along with a multivitamin and pro-biotic that I was able to sneak in, was all he needed. He gained weight, his stool normalized, his runny nose cleared up, and the eczema in his cheeks disappeared.

When it comes to diet, I find that parents are way too concerned about giving children on the autism spectrum variety. Kids don't want variety. They are happy eating the same thing. It is we adults who want variety. The resistance to novelty that is so common with autism can work in the children's favor in this one instance. And, it makes cooking for a GFCF (gluten-free, casein-free) kiddo so much more manageable. I could make the vitamin bread on Saturday, and it would last all week. I'd whip up rice in the rice cooker and pull cooked chicken from the fridge. It couldn't have been easier.

Over the following years, occasionally John would get something with dairy or wheat by accident. He would then become so locked in his own world that he was almost impossible to teach. A stranger once gave him a cookie and glass of milk. Within twenty-four hours, John had broken out in hives all down his neck and back. His ears were bright red. He was so "spaced out" that he kept walking into bushes and would get stuck there and cry. He was completely unteachable, and it took six months before we got him back in our world.

Nothing we did, not even the videos, made the positive impact of this diet change. Sadly, many parents today are not trying the GFCF diet, or they aren't trying it long enough or strictly enough. You must go 100 percent, seven days a week, for at least a year, to know if it is really going to make a difference. I should note that it won't be life-changing for everyone. A study presented at the 2017 International Meeting for Autism Research (IMFAR) found that 70 percent of children do have positive results when they go gluten and casein free. For me, a seven in ten chance that my child could improve significantly is worth the effort of buying something different at the grocery store.

The point is that we eventually got into a routine. A parade of therapists in the home all day was normal. A new way of cooking became the standard. Our weekends were spent in creating "flashcard" videos, and we made it a fun family activity. My husband became accustomed to being awakened at three A.M. if I woke up and suddenly remembered something we needed to film.

We all have routines, and some people are more attached to them than others. Starting something new is only challenging until it becomes a habit, which usually takes a month or so.

It's like swimming in the ocean. The water feels positively freezing when you first jump in, but the activity of paddling and kicking soon warms you up so much that you don't even notice the cold. In fact, it can feel refreshing.

Chapter 6:
"General" Bernard Rimland

D r. Bernard Rimland may be the single most important person in the history of autism research. He was the brigadier who led the charge into the true nature of the disorder, and would inspire my own thinking and advocacy.

Due to the writings of Bruno Bettelheim, until the 1960s autism was considered by many people to have been caused by "lack of parental warmth." It was Dr. Rimland who challenged that hypothesis and revealed the complete lack of research or data to substantiate this claim. He authored the first book to discuss autism as a neurological and biological, rather than a sociological, condition and completely changed the conversation surrounding the disorder. He founded the Autism Society of America, which gave thousands of parents hope, along with relief that they were not the cause of their children's condition.

Dr. Rimland was a visionary, and my mentor.

I met Bernie Rimland at an autism conference in 2002. It was my first conference, and I was determined to show the world what we had done with video-based therapy and the profound effect it had had. Armed with a "before and after" VHS tape of John and a portable VCR-equipped television, my husband and I wandered around the conference ready to talk to anyone who would listen.

It was a very exciting time in autism. Time Magazine had just featured autism as its cover story. The world was waking up to the epidemic, and a handful of doctors, were making huge strides in its treatment. There was a positive energy and hopefulness that we were "this close" to finding a cause and a cure. Thousands of parents attended conferences, and all of them wanted to talk to this one doctor, Jeff Bradstreet, for just five minutes. My husband and I were some of those parents.

Dr. Bradstreet was one of the first doctors to look at the commonalities in biological anomalies with autism. He had developed a treatment plan that included medical tests for gut health, heavy metals, and a host of markers that could be addressed individually, thus improving the overall health and outcomes of his patients. His practice had grown so quickly that he had a long waiting list, and parents were desperate to get an appointment.

Brian and I sought him out at the conference, but he was constantly mobbed. We couldn't get next to him. So, I decided to just set up my little TV in the middle of the hall and start playing John's video. If I couldn't get to Bradstreet, at least I could help some parents who were as frantic as I had been.

The video started out with John sitting on my lap. My husband was cameraman, and he said, "Hi, John." Onscreen, I lifted John's head to look toward Daddy. I raised John's hand, waved it for him, and said, "Hi, Daddy!" John was unresponsive—obviously, completely and utterly lost in his own world, and indifferent to what was going on around him. The film then jumped to one week later. It was shot after John had seen the video we created to help him to respond to greetings and to his name. He was playing a game I'd invented that went like this:

A group of children stood in line waiting their turn.

I called out, "Nicholas!" And then Nicholas would look at the camera and say, "What?"

I said "Hi!" And then Nicholas would wave and say, "Hi!"

Next, I gave a series of commands—walk, stop, sit down, stand up, walk, run—and Nicholas would follow the commands on camera. One after another, the other children followed the same routine.

After John and Lucy had watched their siblings in this video for a week, we tried the game with them. John said, "Hi!" He said, "What?" He followed every command. And we caught it all on camera.

Just one week had passed between the video footage of the lifeless lump on my lap, and this laughing, responsive, little boy—who looked like any typical three-year-old playing Simon Says.

One by one or in pairs, parents at the conference started to crowd around my TV. I heard them say, "Yep, that looks just like my son," in the beginning of the video. When they saw the "after" portion, they gasped. They cried. They screamed. They all wanted to know what we had done. Before long, word got out around the conference, and we were surrounded by hundreds of parents and Bernie Rimland stood in the middle of everyone. He pulled me aside and wanted to hear exactly what we had done, how we were doing it, and how John's progress had been since. He wanted to know all about the twins, about their development and health history.

And he wanted to introduce us to Jeff Bradstreet.

And not only to Dr. Bradstreet, but to Raun Kaufman, whose parents had developed SonRise therapy, and Karynn Seroussi, whose book on the GFCF diet had been so inspirational. All the conference headliners were now standing around my TV watching John.

That moment was the first time I had that special feeling of purpose that would consume my life. I understood that autism was no longer a cross, but a gift. It was given to our family so that we could help others. I didn't have any idea how this was going to happen, but I knew it had to happen. Dr. Rimland felt it, too, and he hounded me for the next few years to write a book. Sadly, he passed away in 2006. It took me sixteen years, but he finally got his wish.

Chapter 7:
The Ethnic Minorities Of China

I needed to hear from autistic people themselves how they perceived the world, how they learned, and what motivated them. I spent the following months seeking out adults on the spectrum who could explain to me. I learned that we all have the same emotions and reactions, but for different stimuli and in different intensities. This was best illustrated by a brilliant woman who set me straight on eye-contact. During our conversation it was clear that she was having trouble maintaining eye-contact despite her best efforts. I just came out with it and told her that my son wouldn't look at us and I needed to understand why. She said that any neuro-typical person knew exactly what it felt like. She, and other autistic people feel the tightness in their chest and anxiety that a typical person feels when looking someone in the eyes when telling a bald-faced lie. In short, it is the feeling of intense shame.

Shame is one of the most uncomfortable and downright terrible feelings in the world. I suddenly understood why my son avoided looking at us, and why when he was being silly or in raucous play, he was distracted from this shame feeling and then had no problem at all making eye-contact. Constantly saying, "Look at me" every 10 minutes in therapy now seemed counterproductive as we were calling attention to this "yucky" feeling. I realized that if we had any hope at improving eye-contact we had to be sneaky about it. We switched to "guerilla" therapy by handing him objects across the line of sight. Daddy played a game called "tickle monster" where he would lay still until John came and looked at him in the eyes, which would awaken the Daddy monster. As the years went on, I became a sort of robot that only spoke when looked at. So, if John asked me a question, I would only answer if he held eye-contact. He didn't know I was intentionally doing this, and his eye-contact is now typical.

Through these conversations with adults on the spectrum, I gained empathy and understanding which became the foundation for what would become Discrete Video Modeling (DVM), the Gemiini method of video instruction.

In 2003, John and Lucy went through the battery of lab tests that are now the standard for a biomedical approach to an autism diagnosis. The results were almost bittersweet, as nearly all were negative. It was a relief that there weren't any difficult underlying physical ailments, but it would have been nice to have more information to work with.

The one test that was positive was for food allergies. John was allergic to milk, refined sugar, peas, chickpeas, peanuts, egg yolks, and all fruit except melon. Lucy was allergic to much the same as well as lamb, but she could have fruit and eggs. Switching to the gluten and casein–free diet had been miraculously positive, and removing these other foods was relatively easy. After these foods were removed, we did see additional benefits. Both children seemed more present. Lucy's irrational defiance just for defiance's sake subsided, and she started to make real strides in academics. John was much more present during therapy, which meant he remembered what he learned. By the time they were in kindergarten, Lucy was mainstreamed without any aid at all. John had a full-time aide until he was in third grade, when all supports were dropped.

Both twins had caught up to peers and no longer qualified for special education services. We enrolled the whole family in a homeschooling co-op that allowed everyone to attend traditional school for two days a week, while having most of their education at home. And I do mean the whole family, as I even sat in with them in classes. Homeschooling isn't for every family, nor for every child—I get that. My eldest five all happened to be self-motivated and sailed through their curriculum a lot faster than their peers in school. Nicholas and Matilda were taught together, just for convenience, and they both entered college early (Nicholas at sixteen, and Matilda at fourteen).

A love of reading certainly contributed to academic success. Funnily enough for a family whose very survival was dependent on video, we weren't really a "video" family. We never had cable TV and rarely watched movies. Instead, we had a two thousand volume book collection that was the center of our entertainment. This vast and varied library allowed the children to study subjects that interested them, in a more in-depth way than traditional high school studies. For example, when Nicholas was fifteen, he scored in the top 0.5 percentile in the nation in science. Nicholas was never taught a formal science course. Instead, he had a science encyclopedia outside the bathroom and took a volume in with him once a day. Everyone must use the bathroom, so might as well make the time count!

This idea of multitasking and optimal use of time was the foundation of my teaching philosophy. When we traveled, the kids watched the Sister Wendy art history program or animal documentaries. We played classical music in the home during the day. I purchased video lectures from universities that we watched while we cleaned. As a result, the Kasbar family has always had a reputation for knowing a prodigious amount of arcane facts, and we can, admittedly, be rather pedantic—for which I apologize profusely to my friends and acquaintances—but we really can't help it.

* * *

As far as academic decisions with the twins, teaching John and Lucy to read at four years old was one of the best decisions I made. Once again, we taught them through video, and they learned the sounds of the letters before John had enough receptive speech to understand what he was reading. By the time he was six, he had his nose in a book every waking minute outside of therapy or school. He was not hyperlexic, as he had to be taught like any typically developing child. He learned all his vocabulary from the videos we made, or books, and he learned it a lot faster than he would have from his environment. This is because he really didn't learn from his surroundings until he was sixteen or seventeen years old. The pull of his inner world was still quite strong, and it distracted him from paying attention in class. In books or video, however, he was a master student.

We noticed that John started to take a real interest in geography, so for

Christmas when he was eight years old, we got him an historical atlas. It taught all the countries in the world, with their historical names and reasons why they had changed names or borders. This became a combination of a bible and security blanket for John. The book went everywhere with him. He could look at any outdated map and name the year it was made. He knew every river, every capital, every mountain range and sea. To be clear, John is not a savant. He must study just like anyone else. It was just that since we didn't have TV, books were our entertainment and his pastime. To this day, he can identify all the flags of the world and the capitals for even the most obscure countries.

The juxtaposition of John's prognosis at diagnosis and where he ended up at nine years of age couldn't have been more diametrically opposed. This was rather humorously illustrated when my husband asked all the children what they wanted him to bring back for them from a business trip to China. Nicholas asked for a small terra-cotta soldier, Matilda and Lucy asked for unusual jewelry, Anthony wanted clothes.

John yelled out, "Get me a book on the ethnic minorities of China!"

This was such an expected sort of request from John that no one even blinked, except the tutor. The guy was laughing so hard, we all stared at him. He could barely speak as he explained, "The funniest thing is not that a nine-year-old wants a book on the ethnic minorities of China, but that none of you even batted an eye!"

Chapter 8:
Locked In A Closet

The years went by, but Dr. Rimland's urging to write a book was always in the back of my mind. I told myself that I would do it once my own kids were grown, but to be honest, I never really believed that anyone would read it. My urgency for the project grew considerably when I received a disturbing email from a dear friend.

She wrote to tell me that her brother's son was recently diagnosed with autism. He lived in Paris, and they had seen some sort of specialist who told the parents to lock the boy in a closet every day for several hours.

I was shocked beyond words, and furious. This practice was positively prehistoric. How could it still be going on? Then I realized that most, if not all, of the newest information on autism was published in English only. There were parents and even professionals around the world who were still living in the middle ages. Suddenly, I felt a deep sense of guilt and shame. Why had I waited so long to do anything? Who had suffered due to my procrastination? Writing a book would take too long, and this called for action NOW. I needed to let the world know that I had a solution.

Before Facebook, there was A Small World. It was a similar sort of social networking site, except it was by invitation only and so had a higher sense of security and privacy. There were message boards where one could post information or comments that the entire community of several hundred thousand people around the world could read. Somewhere in all those people, someone must be struggling with autism.

My post went something like this: "If anyone is dealing with an autism diagnosis, please contact me. My own twins were nonverbal, and now they are mainstreamed without aids and are independent. I have a solution, and I will help at no cost."

Within a few hours I got a reply. I spoke to the mother on the phone and told her that if she bought my ticket, I would not charge anything at all. I just wanted to help. Two days later I had a ticket to London.

I spent a week with the family of a boy named Vincent and showed them how to make the videos. Little Vincent responded right away and started to speak. His mother was elated and begged me to stay in London, but I told her that leaving my six children was well beyond the realm of possibility. I did, however, have a daughter who had grown up making these videos for her siblings and was just finishing college at seventeen years old. So, Matilda went to stay with Vincent and his family for six months and, through her videos, completely changed the course of his life.

At the end of the six months, Vincent was speaking so much that the professionals at the school doubted that he had ever actually been autistic. One might have been tempted to believe them was it not for his mother's next comment. She was from Venezuela and her husband was from Belgium. They lived in London. With all of these various accents in little Vincent's life, he had an American accent! Clearly, he was learning, rather exclusively, from the videos Matilda had created.

Over the years we have found that although children do start out with an American accent when watching Gemiini, they all switch to their parents' accent as soon as the family starts to use the new words they are learning. As Matilda lived with the family and was his primary source of interaction, he retained an American accent until she left.

In the months that followed my trip to London, I traveled around the world and taught families to make the videos. The children responded well while I was there, but very few of the families continued to make videos after I left.

I realized then that I had been a bit overzealous.

Looking back at our old videos, many of them had my eyes half closed as I struggled to stay awake at three o'clock in the morning. We had spent weekends making videos and had a team of actors in our own family. These other families didn't have older children to help and weren't going to spend all weekend or all night making videos. It was just too much to ask of the average person. There was only one solution: I had to make all the videos myself.

* * *

To do this, we were going to need investment, and there was little to no hope of getting grants. Grants also took far too long to secure, even if they were possible to attain—and there were children and families who needed help now.

My husband's boss at the time was a Swedish entrepreneur whose businesses were all named after constellations. I wanted to pitch him my idea of a video-based therapy program, and I hoped to pique his interest with a familiar name. Gemini is a constellation that also mean twins in Latin, and even though he never did invest, the name stuck (we added the double ii in the middle for John and Lucy.)

About that time, my husband and I were invited to a friend's sixtieth birthday on his animal preserve in South Africa. It was one of the most memorable weekends of our lives: a four-day stay with 160 people, all dressed in Out of Africa period costume. We rode with zebra on horseback, went on hot-air balloon rides over the savannah, and dined in gigantic tents lit by crystal chandeliers and silver candelabras. Dire Straits and Johnny Clegg were flown in to perform on a massive stage reminiscent of something from Central Park. And I was pitching the heck out of Gemiini to anyone and everyone who would listen.

The only cellular service in the game preserve was high on top of a cliff that overlooked the festivities. A helicopter would take people up to the cliff to enjoy the incredible vistas. What they saw texting across their phones was even more incredible, but not in a good way. Most of these party-goers were in the financial world, and just then, the financial markets were crashing before their eyes.

It was the beginning of the credit crash that inspired the movie The Big Short, and there was nothing any of us could do about it in the middle of the African wilderness. A dark comedy set over the party, as the guests seemed to decide, "If this is my financial ruin, I might as well enjoy myself while I can."

I had received a very positive reaction to Gemiini at the party and had several offers to fund the project. Four days later, no one wanted to spend even a dime on anything that wasn't "food, clothing, and shelter"—and many of them didn't even have a dime. The timing for Gemiini couldn't have been worse.

After several more trips to London with hopes of investment, I was coming up empty. The offers I did receive came from investors who insisted that I charge families over five hundred dollars per month, and I completely refused.

Then an angel named Elisabeth Spaeth came to the rescue.

Anyone whose child has been helped by Gemiini needs to know this name. She is as much to thank for their child's progress as I am. Elisabeth had been in Africa at the event and had been following the progress of Gemiini ever since. Her faith both in the project and in me personally led her to invest enough money to get Gemiini off the ground with a proof-of-concept website and trial. It wasn't a lot of money, but it was a lot of money to her. There were any number of multimillionaires who could have invested in Gemiini and wouldn't even have missed the funds. Of course, this is the way God works isn't it?

Sometimes I think God put me on that dog-and-pony show just to teach me how His will is accomplished: not with the gold of Solomon, but with the widow's mite.

Chapter 9:
Riptide? ...What Riptide?

The tale spanning from our first investment to the launch of Gemiini is a long and not very exciting story. Suffice it to say that creating a program that could treat anyone's speech and language problem in the world, no matter what the diagnosis or ability level, proved to be a lot more challenging than expected.

I will mention a few of the highlights that acted as milestones during the journey. This is not even close to a complete story, but in the interest of time and saving the reader from a lot of nail-biting suspense, I am choosing to be brief. Here is where I must acknowledge my son Nicholas. At only 20 years old and still in college, he dropped just about everything, including pursuing his own career, to help found Gemiini. There is no way I could have done this alone. His support has been crucial all along.

With Elisabeth's investment, we were able to create our first beta site, conduct our first trial, and film our first testimonial video. My naïve level of confidence and trust in timelines should have cost us the project. When anyone who has ever been involved in a tech project or medical trials reads what I did, they will surely be shaking their heads.

I wanted to get some success stories out as soon as possible. Elisabeth's money only got us to proof of concept, and we needed to show that the program worked in a spectacular way to get the attention of investors, especially during the financial reality of the times. I had seen the method work so well with my own children and with the families whom I had helped, that I was, let's just say, "overly optimistic."

I was going to show that Gemiini could teach three children in just two hours. We would film them before and after they watched the videos, and then let the children take the program home for a week, for more practice. Then we'd interview the parents afterwards. This documentary-style video was sure to knock the socks off any investor. The proof-of-concept site construction was planned to take only a month, and we could create enough videos in that time for our purposes.

The date of completion for the site was set for May fifteenth, and not wanting to waste any time, I set the trial for the next day. This one mistake alone could have derailed everything. Those with experience in tech know that nothing is ever delivered on time. My second mistake is that I didn't even have any children lined up for the trial!

That week, I was in a boutique and overheard the owner talking about her son. Jason was eight years old, had been diagnosed with autism at 3 years old, but was now verbal. He was unable to read despite years of therapy. My first recruit! I approached the woman about including him in the study, and she said yes. One down and two to go.

The project manager on the website told me that her hair stylist's son, Joey, was five years old and practically nonverbal. He had been diagnosed with autism a couple years earlier and had not responded as hoped to school-based therapy. Joey's mom was happy to join, and I was getting closer.

A friend's mortgage broker had mentioned that her son Owen's preschool teacher had suspected he had autism. Owen was seeing a clinical psychologist the next week for a diagnosis. I called Owen's mom and asked if I could meet her. She had been in denial about autism and had even been indignant at the teacher's mention of it. I think, deep down, she knew it was true, but she was just too terrified to admit it. We planned to meet that week.

When I walked into the room, Owen was lying on the floor, holding a Matchbox car up to the corner of his eye, slowly spinning the wheels. This is one of the most common traits in a child on the autism spectrum, and it is never, ever seen in neurotypical children. I could tell that his mother didn't think anything of this, and that she was as oblivious to the signs of autism as I had been all those years ago. I asked her about Owen's language, and she said, "Oh, he talks all the time!"

"What does he say?" I asked. She said that he mostly repeated lines from his movies. I asked if he ever told her what he wanted or used original speech.

She stared at me and said, "Oh, I see what you mean. No, he doesn't." I could see that the denial was dropping as, one by one, I asked the same questions that had been asked of me all those years ago. Finally, she looked at me and said, "So, you think Owen is autistic?"

I eyed Owen on the floor and said, "Do you see what he is doing there? I have never seen a typically developing child do that. But I see autistic kiddos do that all the time."

Her eyes filled with tears, and she broke down. The denial was over, and the grief was setting in right in front of me.

I told her that everything was going to be okay—that her life was going to be crazy for the next few years, but that since Owen was producing speech, there was a great chance that he would be speaking with meaning. I told her of John's and Lucy's success, and advised her not to listen to anyone when they said he would be disabled his whole life. Owen had eczema, and his overall appearance reminded me a lot of John at that age. I explained the GFCF diet and helped her mother go through her cupboards.

She reacted perfectly to the news. She didn't get mad at me. (Once, when I insinuated that someone's child was on the spectrum, I was threatened with getting beaten by a baseball bat—even though the child did, indeed, eventually get an autism diagnosis.) After an hour, the sadness in this woman's eyes had been replaced with hope and a fighting spirit. I remembered what I had been told by that teacher years ago: "The best indicator of a child's prognosis is the fight in the parent." I do know, that despite every effort in the world made by some parents, there are children who will not progress as John and Owen did. There is no guarantee, that is for sure. All we do is tip the odds in our favor when parents fully immerse themselves in the child's therapy.

I knew in my gut that Owen would be fine, and my gut was right. Three years later, MSNBC news did a special on Gemiini and showcased Owen. On the news, he was talking about his playground at school. It was adorable. He was amazing.

Scientists and researchers are probably cringing right now, knowing the insanity of this scenario. Researchers don't just pick subjects completely at random and film a trial before doing a pilot study. Researchers specifically choose the subjects whom they know will be the best candidates for success. They may choose them at random from a specific pool of candidates with defined characteristics, but never quite literally off the street. What was I doing, thinking that I could teach a kid to read in two hours who hadn't been able to read in four years? And working with a five-year-old who had been diagnosed when he was two! This was a child who had had the very best of biomedical intervention and still had almost no expressive speech. Did I really believe that he would talk in two hours with Gemiini? And, not only talk, but identify prepositions, which were rather abstract?

Truthfully, yes, I did believe that. Like a surfer heading to the water with "WARNING RIPTIDE" signs all over the beach, I was running with board in hand, my only thoughts of getting to that outside break as fast as I could.

Chapter 10:
The Most Amazing Day

By an act of pure Divine Providence, I had my three subjects, but I didn't have a website. In fact, on the day of delivery, it wasn't ready. A camera crew had been scheduled for the following day, rooms for the trial were secured. All the content had been filmed, including a reading program. The developers assured me that the site would be up and ready that day. But, at five A.M., we still had no website—and the first subject was set to arrive at eight A.M.

I got on the phone with the project manager. The entire team had been up all night. I heard more promises and kept the faith. At 7:45 A.M. Gemiini came into life, and it was about as perfect as it could be for a proof of concept.

Joey was the first subject. His mother wanted him to be able to play with other children, as she could see that he longed to join in. This had been impossible for him because he was confused by games, as he didn't have language. I decided to film the same "Simon Says" exchange that we had used with John and Lucy to teach them to play an organized game and respond to their names. He did have some receptive language, so we also chose to teach him prepositions, otherwise known as locations words like, "around, "over", and "beside."

We had added in some funny videos to his prepositions to keep his attention, since it was quite a lot to ask a child to watch a learning video for two hours straight. As it turned out, we didn't need those fun videos. As soon as he saw the Discrete Video Modeling (DVM) method that was used in Gemiini, he was absolutely and completely mesmerized. Every time the funny videos came on, he would swat the screen and say, "na, na," as if to try to get rid of them and move on to the learning videos again. He had brought two action figures from home that he obsessively held, one in each hand. These became his props as he acted out each and every preposition, and we caught it all on camera.

At the end of the two hours, Joey came out into the assessment room, so we could film the results. Joey played the Simon Says game perfectly. It was the first time in his life that he'd been able to play an organized game with other children. He beamed with joy, and so did his mother as she watched.

Next came the preposition test. This one was going to be trickier, for Joey had to show me that he understood each word by acting it out with several objects. Not only did he act out every one perfectly—he even *said* every preposition out loud! I find the video of myself at Joey's assessment particularly hysterical, as I am OUT OF MY MIND with excitement on camera each time he gets something right.

Inside, I was thinking that not only was my belief in the method rewarded, but the website worked! Of course, no one else knows this backstory, and it just looks like I have lost my marbles.

Over the next week, Joey's progress grew with Gemiini, and the follow-up interview with his parents still makes me cry. His father ended with, "This is going to change my son's life" And he wasn't speaking in hyperbole.

* * *

Owen came in at eleven o'clock that day for his trial. It was just before lunch, so he brought a lot of food with him. At three years old, his attention span was very limited. He had been kicked out of several preschools for being disruptive to the other students and not being able to follow directions. We decided that one hour was about all he would be able to handle. We wanted to teach him our modified Simon Says game, to see if he could, finally, line up and follow commands. This time, the funny videos we filmed as reinforcement were necessary, and they, along with the food piled on his high chair tray, kept his attention.

At the end of the hour, he came into the assessment room, ran straight to the other children standing in line, and waited his turn to "perform." On cue, he said, "What?" He said, "Hi!" He walked, sat down, stood up, and ran when asked. His mother was elated, and so was the cameraman. This man had been very skeptical about the entire thing. He liked me and liked the story, but he really didn't believe that a bunch of videos could do anything like teach an autistic kid to talk. I turned to look at him, and he was in tears, talking on the phone to someone and saying, "Oh, my gosh, it works! It really works! These kids are talking!"

When Owen's parents came back for their follow-up interview, they brought video they had taken of Owen over the week. Owen was loving Gemiini and was already saying so many things. Most importantly, he was generalizing the content to his own world. From the video cue, "James, what are you doing?", Owen asked his father, "Daddy, what are you doing?" He responded to his name when called. His parents now had so much hope that they no longer feared the word autism.

Next came Jason, who was without a doubt my biggest "Hail Mary" case ever. My sixth child, James, had not yet been identified as dyslexic, and I didn't know much about the condition at all. I had never used Gemiini to teach dyslexia, which this child clearly had in a profound way. I just knew that John and Lucy learned to read this way, and if they could learn to talk (which seemed much more difficult to me than reading), this kid could learn to read.

On top of autism and dyslexia, Jason had the worst case of attention deficit hyperactivity disorder, better known as ADHD, that I had ever seen. He couldn't sit still for two minutes. I must admit that my faith waned to the point of despair after the first thirty minutes. I comforted myself with the idea that we had filmed two incredible successes earlier that day. But, remarkably, Jason wasn't losing interest. He was fidgety beyond belief, but he was not losing interest! He was under the chair, upside down in the chair, and on top of the chair. We had to stop four times just to do jumping jacks.

I noticed something that led me to better understand ADHD. In the four years that he had been in reading therapy, Jason had only learned the sounds of a few letters. His teacher had told his mother that he was incapable of learning phonics and needed to memorize each word individually. Now, English has an alphabet for a reason. Jason was never going to get past middle school academically if he had to rely on memorizing each individual word.

The first letter-sound presented was Mm. Before the model even came on screen, Jason was making the mmmm sound. I thought to myself, "That must be one of the letters he knows." The next sound was for the letter Nn. I watched Jason once again make the mmmm sound. When the model came on the screen and showed a close-up of an open mouth with tongue pressed behind the upper teeth, Jason stopped and almost did a double-take. I could see that he realized he had been making the wrong sound for the letter Nn. After that, he watched carefully as each sound was formed through close-ups of the mouth.

I got the idea that, through his ADHD and autism aversion to eye contact, Jason had actually not been looking at his teacher all these years. He was probably looking around the room and just relying on what he heard. This fits with what I have been told by speech therapists about Gemiini increasing eye contact in therapy sessions. Speech-language pathologist Jennifer Marron writes, "Some students were not willing or able to look at my face. But after watching Gemiini, they seem to be able to sit and participate in one-to-one therapy, and they are making significant gains now."

So, for Jason, who was not seeing the words formed, the similar Nn and Mm sounds were probably indistinguishable. More than likely, he was frustrated and confused that people kept telling him that he was "getting it wrong," when he thought he was repeating what he'd heard.

When he finally got to *see* what he heard with Gemiini, the world of reading suddenly made sense. At the end of the hour, he sat down under a table and read an entire book. It was an introductory-level title from the Bob series, kindergarten level, but that didn't matter. He didn't care. He was on cloud nine, and he was finally going to learn how to read.

We followed up with Jason four weeks later. He had mastered three more books and was getting through the series. His behavior at school had improved, and he was stopping anyone he knew to show them that he could read.

With three for three, the waves receded. I was safely back on shore, and I slept well that night for the first time in a month.

Chapter 11:
The World

Even after releasing this amazing documentary, with the global recession, it took three more years to get the funding we needed to move forward. The highs and lows of those three years could fill a book on their own. With funding came more filming and a new, more robust website. My husband Brian joined the company as his skills in finance and accounting were a missing skill set from our team. I knew that Gemiini was going to be controversial, and I absolutely had to have clinical trials completed and published before launching to the public.

The first pilot study was with a teaching classroom for Gonzaga University. Six of these children had low verbal abilities and two who were non-verbal despite three years in an intensive program. After five months with Gemiini, these two children not only gained language, but were speaking in sentences. Next came a larger preschool study with Spokane Public Schools, in which different classroom styles were compared. It was found that the efficacy of Gemiini in the classroom differs drastically depending on how the teacher uses it, and this study produced the classroom protocols. Portland State University conducted a randomized clinical trial in the Inglewood School District in California and showed that Gemiini was 300 percent more effective than standard video modeling. Ontario Montclair School District conducted one of the largest studies in autism, with over 160 children. This study showed that Gemiini could teach receptive and expressive language to more severely affected children who had not been able to learn after years of therapy and classroom teaching. Two of these studies are currently in peer review, and one is published.

Due to the death of the editor of the journal, the Portland study took two years to publish after it was accepted for publication. Two years of waiting to launch and two years of children not receiving this life-changing therapy almost killed me. The wait was agonizing, but I just didn't have the choice to launch prior to publication. We had to have several more rounds of funding to get to launch, but by the grace of God, we made it. And when we did launch, it was almost by accident.

Dr. Maria Gilmour, who was the researcher on the Portland State study, just happened to find a paper that had been published about Gemiini without our knowledge. The abstract didn't mention Gemiini by name, and so it didn't come up in searches. Portland study still didn't have a publication date, but we had our first published study!

And, oh, what a study it was! The researchers were professors from three universities, including the former Director of Clinical Psychology for Princeton. The study subjects were all adults, which was very rare in autism research; nearly all other study subjects are small children. These findings showed that Gemiini's Discrete Video Modeling method was effective at teaching not only language, but articulation and reading, which were more firsts for video modeling in general. The researchers included a survey for the teachers who had administered the trial. Teachers are notorious for not implementing novel therapy approaches, and I can't really blame them. Most approaches are created in clinics under sterile conditions and don't hold up under the chaos of the classroom. All the teachers surveyed said they would continue to implement Gemiini after the trial and that it was easy to use.

Even I, in my wild optimism, wouldn't have dreamed up a study like this. I could finally get it to the public! But how? There was so much snake oil out there now with autism. Would anyone really believe me? How would I get their attention? How could I get parents, weary of spending thousands on empty promises, to give it a chance?

* * *

I wrote a script that told the entire Gemiini story in eight minutes to accompany the before-and-after video of John. It warned parents that many kiddos don't like the videos at first. I encouraged them to have their children watch during meals and not to give up! It was a message of hope and, more importantly, offered proof that the program worked. We embedded the video on the website home page and on our Facebook page. I paid about fifty dollars to advertise the video to people in the U.S. who had something to do with autism. Within a few hours, we had our first Gemiini members.

Our Facebook likes started to climb. Within a week, we were signing up dozens of new members each day. Testimonials were coming in. Parents were videoing their children talking. The whole enterprise was growing in leaps and bounds, until it was almost out of control. The website still had a lot of bugs, and we had to create workaround solutions on the fly to prevent service lapses to members. The website started to look like a patchwork quilt of pieced-together buttons, but parents were forgiving. They knew it was working for their children, and that we were working as fast as we could too.

What was more, the Gemiini community was coming together online. Parents and professionals were helping and encouraging each other. The news outlets were calling us for interviews. The dream was becoming a reality!

Five months after we launched, I received a message from Mary Kay Deal, the mother of a child with Down syndrome. She wanted to start a private support page just for families with DS who were using Gemiini. Her page grew by hundreds of people each week, and now—years later—it is "Gemiini Central" for thousands of families using the program, no matter the diagnosis of their child. The community came full circle in another way: mothers who were grateful for their children's success with Gemiini quit their jobs to work for us. These mothers make up our product specialist team. They spend hours every day speaking with other parents and giving them tips and tricks to make the program as efficacious as possible.

Gemiini has been filmed in American Sign Language, Australian Sign Language, French, Chinese, Spanish, and Arabic. It is used in over forty countries.

The snowballing popularity did not go unnoticed by the media; I have appeared on CBS, NBC, ABC, and HLN, and the Orange County Register named me as one of the 100 Most Influential People in Orange County, California.[ii]

Additionally, Gemiini has been featured by CNN, the U.K. Independent, and many more journals and periodicals. I have lectured to members of the Jordanian Ministry of Health and the Mexican Department of Education. I even gave a twenty-minute lecture in Spanish to the Mexican Congress.

Today, Gemiini is a modern marvel of both efficacy and tenacity. I have people chase me down at autism conferences to tell me through their tears of happiness how grateful they are for hearing their children's voices. You would think that I would, finally, be content.

Nope.

I still sit up at night thinking about those children who haven't tried it, or almost worse, whose parents quit too soon. I know why they quit, but I don't know how to get them not to quit.

About 5 percent of Gemiini kiddos start to speak within the first few minutes of seeing the program. Their parents are overcome with joy. They film their children like crazy and post all over social media. It is through these little miracles that Gemiini has grown so fast. After seeing a parade of miracles across their newsfeeds over several months, even the most downtrodden parents who have tried everything are willing to give it a go. The problem is that most autistic people take longer than a few minutes to talk, and despite begging and pleading, most parents do not test their children receptively.

Language is divided into what we understand, or receptive speech, and what we say, or expressive speech. Nearly everyone learns receptively with Gemiini in the first few months, but expressive speech is another thing entirely. Many people with autism or Down syndrome have apraxia, or "dyspraxia of speech," as it is called in the UK and Australia.

Apraxia used to be called mutism years ago, and most people still know it by that name. There is a long and complicated explanation of what it is, and what it is not from a neurological point of view. As Dr. William Mobley, Director of Neuroscience at UCSD said, "The important thing is that we know that Gemiini works, finding out why it works is more academic than practical." But the quick definition is not being able to speak, even though you know what you want to say. Some speech therapists won't even accept clients with an apraxia diagnosis, as it is very difficult to treat.

Gemiini has been shown to be one of the only methods— and by far the easiest—to treat speech apraxia. But, it takes time, and no one can tell you exactly how long it will take for your particular child. We have seen some children with apraxia start to talk the first week, but many more take months or even years. Above all, parents and professionals need to avoid the temptation to project their own learning experience on people with apraxia. Too many assume, "If he has seen this video a thousand times and he still can't say it, he is never going to say it." Gina Pope has a background in special education, so she knew her son's triumph over apraxia was going to be a marathon, not a sprint. She writes:

> My youngest son (7) has severe apraxia and ASD. He has been in therapy since he was 23 months. We started Gemiini right before his 5th birthday. It took 2 years to get vocals in the form of words and phrases. He now has 21 spontaneous words and a few "I want" phrases. Best news is we have approximations and verbal attempts on almost everything now. This vocal expression has all been in the last few months.

> You may wonder why I stuck it out for two years, or if in fact if it was Gemiini that caused this language burst. But I can tell you Gemiini is a key component to his growth. Because of my background in child development and education I knew the other measures of success—not just verbal language. 1. Eye contact and awareness. That improved within weeks of using Gemiini. 2. His imitation skills. Gemiini was critical at helping teach motor and vocal imitation. 3. Receptive language.

> The growth in his receptive language was immense and immediate. Animals, body parts, appliances, community helpers, instruments, shapes, letters, numbers, etc. etc., we did it all, and he learned it all!!! I knew if we just kept improving his receptive the expressive would come.

Last but not least, I measured his reading. My son may not speak, but with Gemiini we helped him read. He can read words at the 2nd and 3rd grade level...which is amazing!!!

I guess my point is sometimes success is not measured in the way we assume. Some of us moms need to know success for us right now may not be vocal, but the fact that he will follow you banging a drum or learning to identify a rhombus. Gemiini is an Arsenal. For some it's a cannon the blows right through, for some of us, it's a trench digger...but hey I love getting dirty, and either way we can get to the other side.

Sometimes it happens that once the child starts to talk, the words come faster, and they are saying twenty new words a month. Sometimes they will only add one new word a month. But in nearly all cases, understanding is improving dramatically. And once the person understands, they can learn to read and to write or type.

You see, the important thing is to give the person a means to communicate. If it isn't through expressive speech, then typing or sign language is a life-saver. But, if the person doesn't have enough receptive language, none of these alternative communication methods will work. Receptive language is the most important building block, and most parents don't understand this. In fact, when parents finally venture to test to their children's receptive language, they are amazed at how much they are learning from Gemiini. It gives them hope and the mental strength to carry on. That being said, we never stop working for expressive speech. I have seen it come after three years of Gemiini, even though years of traditional speech therapy didn't produce results.

Unlike almost any other method known (and certainly anything so widely available and affordable), Gemiini is effective even with older people who have apraxia. Janine Roberts from Australia writes:

> Our 19 year old daughter, Stef had about 4 words she used regularly, despite having spent most of her life in therapy. These words were not clear but we knew what they meant. Within a week of starting Gemiini, she had picked up 3 new words and said them clearly, after another week, 2 more.

> So now, 6 months later, she has about 40 words she can say, she has gained more eye contact, tries harder to participate in activities and with prompting is trying to say new words all the time. She is watching our mouths when we speak. She is still shy about speaking, and rarely speaks to anyone unless she is particularly motivated (usually by food) but every word is an absolute gift and one step closer to being able to communicate her needs and wants to us all.

As automated as we have tried to make Gemiini in its subsequent iterations, it is almost impossible to make a "plug and play" version suitable for every person on the planet. For some people, it is necessary to venture to the complete video library to create videos from our clips, which can be tailored to the specific person's needs. This is especially true of people who have a large discrepancy in their receptive and expressive language, or who are older. For these members, it is best for parents, therapists, or caregivers to get on a call with our specialists, so they can be pointed in the right direction.

I wish that everyone could see what I have witnessed with this program— and get all parents to test their children's weekly receptive gains like we did with the twins. I wish they could understand the underlying neurological effects and that they could feel confidence in the process of learning. I want to tell them, "Just dive in! The waves may look scary, but it is so beautiful out here in the surf you will never regret venturing out. Sometimes it seems like an eternity between sets. But, just hang in there! The big one is worth the wait."

Chapter 12:
And I Thought AUTISM Was Tough...

Had I only five children, I would have sworn that my nontraditional way of schooling was the key to producing a scholar. Child number six taught me just how wrong I was! James was the boy in the nursery rhyme that goes, "Snakes and snails and puppy dog tails, that is what little boys are made of." He climbed a fifty-foot tree at three years old (much to my horror). He would crawl out the windows of our house and onto a very steep roof, so we had to lock the windows to keep him in. He never wore shoes, even out in the forest. He could catch any critter he set his sights on. He earned the nickname "Huckleberry," and true to his namesake, he had no interest in reading whatsoever.

He learned the sounds of the individual letters with ease, so I initially thought reading was going to be a home run. Years went by and he still wasn't a fluid reader. At eight years old, he was assessed and found to have profound dyslexia. I felt like a complete failure as a mom. How did I miss this for so long?

We tried several different dyslexia programs, but none were realistic, due to his ADHD. He just couldn't focus long enough and I was not going to medicate him.

After the success with the twins, my answer to every problem was "Make a video!" It was from working with James that the Gemiini Reading program was born.

I needed to produce something that could be viewed while he was jumping on a trampoline or swinging from the ceiling. It had to work on a neurological level. Hooked on Phonics was great to "get kids by," but it wasn't going to influence the underlying brain function that was causing the problem. Through research, I found that dyslexia can be every bit an auditory processing disorder as a reading problem. I believed this to be the case with James, as he could name any letter sound, but when the letters were strung together, he couldn't sound out a complete word. I needed him to "see" and hear the sounds in a continuous way.

By using the Discrete Video Modeling method of filming close-ups of the mouth and creating a reading series with progressively more complex phonemes, I hoped to train James's brain to see and hear the sounds of the letter combinations simultaneously. The greatest thing about it was that he could watch videos in the car or while he was eating. Thankfully, he didn't have to just sit and focus, because that simply wasn't possible.

Teaching James to read in this manner wasn't an overnight success. It took nearly as long as it did to teach John to talk, but it worked. He started to read fluently. He caught up to his peers. And now, at seventeen, he reads complex postgraduate material on the financial markets and spends hours researching. As is common with ADHD, the reading material needs to be of high interest for him to stay focused and not have his mind wander—but I'll take that over the prognosis I was given when he was eight years old any day of the week!

* * *

The Gemiini dyslexia and early reading program, I have no doubt, will change the world. Dyslexia wreaks much more havoc on our society than many people realize. The dyslexic brain tends to be highly creative and can multitask exceptionally well. Dyslexic people tend to be brilliant problem solvers. They are disenfranchised from our academic-focused society during school years.

We do not yet have published research with dyslexia, so I don't have statistical data, but it is forthcoming. The anecdotes, however, are jaw-dropping. One case in particular comes to mind.

Mia was a thirteen-year-old girl who was a typical teenager in every way, except that she couldn't read. In fact, she barely knew the sounds of the letters. This was despite her parents spending close to a million dollars on therapy. They literally tried everything to get her to read, until a brain scan at UCLA found that she had "no semantic overlap between her auditory and visual plains." Researchers counseled Mia's parents to stop trying to force her to read and instead to buy her technology that would read for her and would take dictation. They said that no matter what they tried, her brain structure was never going to allow her to read.

The problems associated with total illiteracy go far beyond academics. Our very social society is based on text messages. We need to read everything from road signs to product labels and menus. Mia couldn't do that. Her hair always appeared greasy as her mother found that she'd been using conditioner instead of shampoo, due to not being able to decipher the labels. Mia had to wait until all her friends ordered food at a restaurant and then say, "I'll have what she's having." This problem that total illiteracy causes would only escalate, and escalate considerably, as she got older.

At the end of Mia's seventh-grade year, I was introduced to her mother by a mutual friend. I told her about the Gemiini online program and said that she had nothing to lose to try. She was skeptical to say the least. But, I don't think she could have lived with herself if she didn't at least give Mia the choice to try it. Mia agreed to use Gemiini over the summer, although it was going to be challenging. The family had planned a trip to Greece for several weeks, and Internet service there would be intermittent at best.

Despite all the technical challenges, being on vacation, and the irresponsibility that goes hand-in-hand with being thirteen, Mia somehow managed to watch the videos for about thirty minutes a day. She also kept it up when they got back home and, with the aid of her reading tutor, incorporated more of the Gemiini learning tools into her daily routine.

At the end of six weeks, she had increased her reading by four grade levels.

Her mother claims it is a miracle, and I can't really disagree. The results were more than even I had hoped for. Today, Mia is enrolled in a public high school and takes regular ed classes. She plans on attending university and wants to be an educational counselor to help other children, the way Gemiini and her reading therapists helped her.

* * *

After my experience with James, I was on the lookout when I had Luke, child number seven. By the time he was six months old, it was clear that he wasn't autistic, at least not from birth as the twins had been. But when he started to talk, something was wrong. None of the baby talk sounded anything like the real word. Luke's name for his brother Anthony was "Wobees" and for James was "Tsity," and so on. I learned this was a potential early indicator of an auditory processing disorder, so I started him on Gemiini at fifteen months. By the time he was twenty-two months, his baby talk had progressed to more typical speech, and he was not only intelligible, but advanced. I was hoping that we were out of the woods on dyslexia too, but no dice.

Little Luke is the only one of my children who will go through all his elementary education at school, not at home. We made this decision not from a change of heart about homeschooling, but because we were fortunate to find a new, unique school that was in line with our goals: Chinese. From the time I learned that I was pregnant with Luke, I had planned to teach him Chinese. When he was just a few months old, I would play YouTube videos in Chinese and let them run in the background while he played. Why Chinese? Most people assume I have an interest in the language because China is a rising star in global markets. Although this is a bonus, this isn't the main reason. The main reason is more neurological than anything else. Learning Chinese has direct benefits on recall.

Working memory, or digit span, is the ability to remember information and retrieve it quickly. Intelligence tests have more to do with processing speed than anything else. It has been shown that people with average IQs can come up with the same answers as gifted people, if you just give them enough time.

The Internet is destroying our memory. [iii] Before its invention, the average English speaker had a digit span of seven, which means they could remember seven pieces of information in a list. American phone numbers had seven digits for this reason. Years ago, a professor at Yale University explained to me that people who speak a tonal language like Chinese will often have a digit span up to ten. This researcher believed that the memories of Chinese people grew to accommodate their language, as they must learn not only how the word sounds, but the tone in which it is said. To read, they must memorize each word separately, as they don't have an alphabet. Chinese have developed a legendary work ethic in academics: if you don't work hard, you don't learn how to read.

Due to today's technology memorizing everything for us, English speakers' digit spans have deteriorated to only four. Which means that our sequential processing never makes it above a typically developing four-year-old child. If you go onto a top U.S. university campus and see a majority of Asian faces, this may be one of the reasons why. Their memory capability is far superior to those who speak only English.

Without the ability to synthesize information quickly, it takes much longer to solve problems. The longer it takes to solve problems, the longer the problems persist and the more damage they cause. On the macro scale, this isn't really an issue, because through technology we now have many more brains working on problem solving. But, on the micro scale, like the problems that come up in one's own life and in one's own family, it can be devastating. Success in life is defined by how well and how quickly one can solve the everyday problems that arise just through existing on this planet. For those with slow processing speeds, problems can pile up and become seemingly insurmountable.

I wonder if this isn't one of the causes behind the meteoric rise in clinical depression, especially among the generation who has been raised with the Internet and technology. Millennials are infamously lacking in problem-solving skills. Most people blame it on their lack of resilience and "grit," but I wonder if it isn't more fundamental. Maybe they honestly can't solve simple day-to-day problems as fast as they arise. The procrastination that this delay creates heaps up so many problems that they are just overwhelmed. They feel helpless and hopeless, which is the root of all depression. The recent research showing that increasing alpha wave activity can decrease depression supports this hypothesis.[iv]

The greater the alpha, the easier the problem solving—hopelessness decreases, and depression is thwarted.

People with learning exceptionalities from autism to Down syndrome to dyslexia typically have poor working memories. This will impede everything from word retrieval (that feeling when you have a word "right on the tip of your tongue") to reading fluency. As children, most of these people are diagnosed with working memory issues during school assessments, but due to the time it takes for traditional remediation methods, the schools rarely, if ever, treat the memory problem. We created the Gemiini working-memory game for this very reason. Students can, on their own, work to improve their digit span, and the results we are seeing with those who play the game faithfully each day have been impressive. I myself have seen my son go from a digit span of two to a seven in eighteen months, which equates to about five years of memory development! As his digit span has increased, his reading and even his behavior at school have improved. He still has a long way to go, but he is making substantial progress.

Not every American kid will learn Chinese. If you really want to get as much as you can from Gemiini for your child, the working-memory game needs to be a part of their daily routine. There is not much point to learning if the student can't remember what they learned.

Chapter 13:
Everything But The Kitchen Sink

Many people ask which therapies or treatments we tried, and which were the most successful. The answer is, we tried just about anything that had any promise at all for the twins' particular issues. Many of these were at great cost with no discernible benefit. Here's what did work:

1. Gluten-free, casein-free diet
2. Gemiini videos
3. Minimum 30 hours per week of live play-based therapy
4. Probiotics (Primal Defense or Thrive)
5. UCLA Program for the Education and Enrichment of Relational Skills (PEERS)
6. Respen-A, a homeopathic topical treatment
7. Magnetic e-Resonance Therapy (MeRT, very expensive and doesn't work for everyone)
8. Neurofeedback

And in that order.

We would never have been able to get anywhere with John if the diet hadn't brought him out of his fog. Live therapy would not have been able to teach him fast enough without Gemiini. He wouldn't have been able to absorb the nutrients in his food without the probiotics. The neurofeedback brought him out of his daydream, though only slightly. The PEERS program taught him social skills as a teenager. Respen-A increased his awareness of himself and his surroundings, similar to what we saw with the GFCF diet, sort of a second awakening.

As far as live therapy, we tried:

- Applied Behavior Analysis (ABA)
- Relationship Development Intervention (RDI)
- Son-Rise
- Floortime
- Speech Therapy (ST)
- Occupational Therapy (OT)
- Physical Therapy (PT)
- Doman Method

What we settled on was a synthesis of all the above, which I would much later learn had been given an acronym all its own: PRT. This "Pivotal Response Therapy" is a fancy term for common sense in therapy. You engage the child in activities that he/she enjoys and use those as opportunities for generalization or teaching. We combined the live PRT with video modeling therapy. Classic PRT alone takes much longer to see results (too long in my opinion), as there are long pauses between learning opportunities. With our method, the teaching of new material was done through video during meals, and so the PRT sessions were devoted to generalization, or practicing in real life what they were learning on the videos.

During the years the twins were in daily therapy, Fridays were the only time we did Discrete Trial Training (DTT), which is traditional table-time therapy with flashcards. That was the day the twins were tested both receptively and expressively on the video content they'd been learning. Friday was always an exciting day, and I would wait eagerly to hear the results of the assessments. I was never disappointed. The twins were learning eighty to ninety percent of their curriculum, so between twenty and forty new words per week and generalizing everything. Even at this, before unheard of, speed of learning, John didn't catch up to peers until he was eight years old.

I often cringe when I hear the metrics for most individualized education programs, or IEPs—(the educational plans that schools create for children with special needs). I have rarely found them to include realistic goals for achieving communicative parity with peers.

Corey Valley used to call our home "the incredible changing program," as she had never seen a child learn so quickly, especially one who had only recently been making no gains for months. Discrete Video Modeling (DVM), is the only method I know of that can teach fast enough to make catching up to peers a reality for many children, especially when considering the low cost.

The last therapy we tried was Magnetic e-Resonance Therapy (MeRT), and it was done when John was eighteen years old. It costs a fortune, and by the company's own admission, it has not shown positive results with everyone.

By that time, John didn't need much more therapy. But, after listening to one of the lead doctors from a prestigious medical center is Los Angeles speak about both the founder and the technology of MeRT in the most glowing terms possible, I wanted to see for myself.

After John's first week, the difference was noticeable. So noticeable, in fact, that I mistook him for his brother when I heard him speaking from the next room. He was chatty, and the inflection in his speech was completely typical. That being said, after trying MeRT for an entire month, we didn't see any additional improvement.

* * *

The CEO of the MeRT program was intrigued by our family history, and he offered to give us all a free brain scan and assessment. These scans measure the combination and relationship of different brain wavelengths. Most people with autism have high theta wave activity, which is associated with dreaming, and this is exactly what John's scan showed. The presence of high Theta waves reinforces the research that proves people on the autism spectrum have a dominant default network, or the part of the brain used for daydreaming and dreaming.[v]

This is likely why they often have that "lost in thought" expression, which is the same expression that any typical person has when they daydream. It is also why Gemiini is more effective than live therapy for direct instruction. Through the unique filming method, Gemiini appears to "wake the viewer up" to teach them in the active part of the brain. Research has shown that even adults on the autism spectrum who had a lifelong inability to remember what they learned were able to retain mastery of information months later, when taught through Gemiini.[vi]

Unlike theta waves, beta waves come into play when we are alert, paying attention, and engaged in a task. Alpha waves are predominant when we are relaxed and resting, and can synthesize the information we learned in beta. Alpha activity is associated with creativity and can reduce the risk for depression. An alpha state is what is created during meditation, for example.

When my own brain scan was analyzed, the doctor found that I had an unusual brain pattern. In fact, among tens of thousands of scans, he had only seen one other instance. Most brain scans produce a visual graph that looks somewhat like a bell curve. Mine, on the other hand, had a double hump. Evidently, my brain produces two alpha peaks. It was almost as if I had two brains that could synthesize information on overtime. It wasn't that I could learn faster, but that I had more brain space dedicated to using the information that I'd learned.

This explained quite a lot. My whole life, I have been able to estimate calculations without working out the problem. It had even become sort of a joke with Brian and me. I would estimate building costs, square feet, mortgage costs—just about anything to do with numbers—in seconds. When we were first married, he would say, "No, that can't be right," take out his calculator, and find the exact number. I was always within 3 percent.

As the years went on, he stopped trying to verify my guesses. He didn't understand my facility, because I am not that great at math. I must do a problem several times to get the same answer twice. My husband, who is a math wiz, would probably whoop the pants off me in a real math test. This ability doesn't have anything to do with my active brain. I used to tell him that I just "feel" the answer. It is like that with all problem solving for me. I just feel the solution, and if it doesn't come to mind immediately, I get into the bathtub and wait for it to come. I must admit; my life has produced a lot of opportunities for crafting solutions— and I have spent a lot of time in the bathtub.

A few months after we had these scans, my husband called, very excited. He said that, just by chance, he had been introduced to the other "double alpha." Evidently, she was so much like me that it was uncanny. She and I did meet, and yes, we are very alike. And she, too, has this unusual capacity for estimating numbers. We both also have an intensity that can be a bit unnerving to more docile types. In fact, I think the two of us, together, are a bit much for any one room. Our husbands teased that they needed to start a "double alpha" support group, but that they would be the only ones in it.

I do believe that MeRT gave John some extra, little push. It may have been slight, but it was enough to get him to the next level—and there isn't another level now. He is truly more functional than most typically developed people. He has a great job and is a stellar employee. He gets high marks in university and loves his classes. He has friends with whom he goes to movies and events, or just hangs out. He is universally loved, and I constantly hear from people in my community what a "fine, young man" he is. And, almost none of these people even know that he was once diagnosed with autism.

Both twins grew to have a facility and love of language. Lucy is finishing her electrical engineering degree. John studied in France and even created his own language using cognates from 27 existing languages (including Xhosa clicks).

Of course, we tried a lot of things that didn't work, and there are many more "treatments du jour" out there now that I haven't tried. Swimming with dolphins, secretin, magnet therapy, and more vitamins than I can remember, didn't move the needle in any significant way. Not that these therapies haven't been useful for others; they just didn't show results that would justify the expense with my own kiddos.

With money and time being two very scarce resources, I would advise starting with the GFCF diet and Gemiini, and then move on from there as resources permit. Be careful. If you try to catch every wave in a set, you risk missing the biggest one.

Chapter 14:
Number-One Son

Once my husband and I had immersed ourselves in autism research and literature, one thing became obvious. Nicholas, our eldest, was squarely on the autism spectrum. He was very high on it, but he was definitely on it. When he was back in the third grade, we had decided to homeschool due to his social issues. He was lightyears ahead academically, as he had spent hours in front of "Teach Your Baby to Read" flashcards from infancy. He had gone to kindergarten at three years old and could read at a high-school level by the second grade. But, he had such profound social issues that the teacher was constantly compelled to instruct the class on how to be kind to Nicholas.

Nicholas would stand inches from the other students, completely unaware of the invisible personal bubble that typical people automatically feel. The last straw at school came when Nicholas stood up in the middle of a lecture, walked over to the window and just stared outside. When the teacher asked him if he would like to take a seat he replied, "No thank you Sister, I already know what you are teaching, and I am really enjoying watching Mr. Strand cut the grass into such interesting geometrical shapes. You should all come and see it!" The entire class jumped up and ran to the window, much to the dismay of his teacher. After the tenth time having to formulate a plan of social inclusion, we decided that school might not be the best place to practice these skills.

Homeschooling allowed Nicholas the freedom to learn what interested him and to grow and mature without the negative social pressures that an "awkward teenager" typically endures. He didn't know why we decided to homeschool him until he was in his twenties. He had friends who, looking back, were also likely on the spectrum and were also homeschooled. Consequently, Nicholas grew up a confident kid with the reputation of the "smart one" instead of the "weird one."

This was best illustrated on the maiden voyage of the Princess Sapphire Cruise Ship. Brian's mother chose to celebrate her sixtieth birthday on a cruise to Alaska and brought the entire family. As this was a "grand opening" so to speak, the guests included many wealthy families of note. The teenagers on the ship attended some of the most prestigious private boarding schools in the country. Heretofore, Nicholas' only experience with kids his own age was with a select group of homeschoolers. He had never interacted with "typical" teenagers, much less teens from East Coast boarding schools. He was nervous, and secretly so was I.

To both of our relief, he fit in perfectly.

Actually, he fit it in better than perfectly. By the end of the trip he was given the nickname "007" and was considered by all to be the "smart and sophisticated" one in the group. He was a super-star, and he knew it. Looking back, I think that was the watershed moment for Nicholas when any social anxiety he had disappeared. When the valedictorian of Andover Academy calls you 'the smart one", it does a lot for one's self esteem. If he could conquer this crowd, he felt that he could do anything.

Over the years, many parents of children who are now adults have expressed regret to me about their traditional schooling. Their children were ignored, or worse, bullied and made to feel insecure. This experience shaped their personalities forever. I know that there is a lot of emphasis being placed on anti-bullying campaigns, but, I wouldn't want my child to be a guinea pig. None of my children have ever been bullied, nor has anyone ever been unkind to any of them in any way. We were fortunate that the Spokane Public School District offered a hybrid school, which homeschoolers could attend two days a week. Many of the kids there were also on the spectrum, and so, we really did have the best of both worlds.

The story of how Nicholas overcame his challenges is the subject of another book entirely, and one he or I will someday write. Suffice it to say, he proved that with a lot of practice, one really can overcome just about **anything**. He still retains the positive aspects of Asperger's (now called HFA), like intellectual curiosity and attention to detail, but is more socially adept than many typical people. Today, Nicholas is COO of Gemiini and active in helping others. One of the proudest moments of my life is when he recently received KultureCity's Advocate of the Year award.

Now, no one believes me when I tell them he is on the spectrum. To that I answer: I have old family movies to prove it.

Chapter 15:
Beyond Autism

Over the years, Gemiini's scope has gone way beyond autism. Children and adults with Down syndrome (DS) have done, in many ways, even better with the program than those with autism. Gemiini appears to allow them to hear themselves more clearly, and parents have reported that even adults with DS will now self-correct their pronunciation of words until they hear themselves say them correctly.

Conventional wisdom says that people with Down syndrome learn to read by memorizing words, rather than by mastering phonics. But, this creates an artificial academic ceiling and prevents people with DS from advancing into high school classes. The Gemiini reading program, which is phonics based, is disproving these assumptions. Silas was the first child with DS to learn to read with Gemiini. His mother writes:

We have been using Gemiini for approx. 2 months with our son (6 years old with DS). His reading and articulation have improved drastically in that short amount of time and we can't wait to see where he goes with this! Since using Gemiini his reading level has probably tripled. He was struggling to read two-vowel words at the end of the school year and now after these 2 months he is probably reading at a 1st grade level. What's so amazing is that we can now UNDERSTAND what he's saying!! He was very hard to understand but with the articulation tools on Gemiini we are amazed by the results. The program is easy to use and it is very effective for kids with Down syndrome who are visual learners like our son. We couldn't be more pleased!

Over the years, there has been a lot of interest in conducting an articulation study with adults with Down syndrome. Many adults with DS will adopt a pattern of social nonparticipation, due to people outside their families not being able to understand them. If something as simple as watching videos can improve articulation enough for intelligibility, this will change lives in a profound way. As we don't yet have published research, I can't say for a fact that this is possible for everyone. But, I can say that I have received letters from many parents saying that is, indeed, what they have witnessed. These are some of my favorite letters to receive because the difference is so stark, and parents tell me that they are discovering their children's true personalities for the first time.

Like anything, an ounce of prevention is worth a pound of cure, and using Gemiini from infancy may correct articulation issues before they take hold. We recommend that people play Gemiini in the background for small children with

DS, even as young as a few months old. This is a tactic called "auditory bombardment" in the speech and language profession. The slowed-down articulation may allow the infant to hear the sounds better—and talking in slow motion all day would drive any parent bonkers if they had to do it themselves.

Gemiini has seen success with people across a whole list of diagnoses. It isn't just an "autism therapy tool" anymore—it is a language, articulation, reading, working memory, task acquisition, social skills, and life skills tool.

Due to all the testimonial videos from excited parents of formerly non-verbal children, many people believe that Gemiini is targeted towards non-verbal people only. Although these cases are some of our biggest successes, they make up only a small percentage of our total members. The Gemiini content goes all the way to university level and the advanced vocabulary can even help with studying for the SAT college placement test.

Crossing the bridge from single word labels to conversational speech is one of the most difficult and potentially agonizing milestones in the language process. It certainly was with our twins. Knowing how difficult this step can be, I have focused particular attention on giving students the tools they need to make crossing this bridge as natural and automatic as possible.

When I first heard John's voice say "puc" I thought that our language journey had come to a successful end. Boy was I mistaken! It was years and years of getting him caught up, and in the end, thanks to video, he ran right past his peers.

Chapter 16:
Tick-Tock

Back in 2000, when the Internet was still relatively new and everyone and his uncle hadn't uploaded their faintest ramblings, there was very little posted on autism. Now there is so much it is often confusing, as people seem to contradict each other. Unfortunately, the one piece of information that is most crucial to parents of newly diagnosed children has been buried: Time is everything.

The earlier you start therapy, the GCFC diet, bio-med, Gemiini, and (fill in the blank), the better it all will work. The twins started the gluten-free, casein-free diet when they were nearly four years old. By that time, enough brain damage had occurred that it took years to heal and reverse. Had they started the diet at eighteen months, or better yet, never had gluten and casein at all, I assure you that you would not be reading this book right now, because there wouldn't be a book. They still may have been diagnosed with autism, but John would likely have responded to ABA the way his sister did, and there would probably have been no need for me to invent Discrete Video Modeling and create Gemiini.

Every day that you wait—every minute, even—their little brains are getting more "stuck in their ways" and harder to mold. Over the last nineteen years, I have spoken to thousands of parents. Of all the parents whose children started intensive therapy before two years old, only a small handful are still dependent today.

In some areas of the world, officials won't even diagnose autism before age five. This is true in many places in the UK, where waitlists for diagnosis can be over a year long.[vii]

Therapists are so scarce in the world that many older people are simply turned away. I know a woman in Australia whose teenage daughter was turned away by over thirty speech pathologists because they felt their limited time was better spent on a young child.

I am constantly surprised how few parents today have the urgency I felt just twenty-four hours after reading about autism. Back then, this message was everywhere. Today it is buried in mommy blogs, biomedical interventions, and a host of other absolutely wonderful information. Don't get me wrong; it isn't that I am against all this new stuff. It is just that the essential is being drowned out.

Children need therapy THE MINUTE a parent suspects a delay. Not a week later, not after a diagnosis, and for heaven's sake, not years later. Eighteen months old is not too early to start. And, at that very minute, Gemiini can provide therapy right in the child's home.

I know I write a lot about getting a therapist on board, but the truth of the matter is, these people aren't on every corner. There is often a longer waitlist for a therapist than for a diagnosis, and they don't come cheaply, either. Gemiini was designed to be "shallow enough for a lamb to bathe in or deep enough for an elephant to swim." The new Gemiini is so user friendly that any technophobe can get started. It is true that the complete video library with over 100,000 videos can be a bit daunting, but that section can be set aside if the parent isn't up to it. The automated assessment does an exceptionally good job at directing the parent to the best starting point for the child. And, if you have any questions at all, our team of support specialists, most of whom are mothers of children with special needs, are free to help in any way they can. For some reason, only 30 percent of our members take advantage of this important service, but those who do, know its value.

All that being said, Gemiini is one of the only therapies that works regardless of age. But "work" is a relative term. We are seeing many young children who start Gemiini before three-and-a-half years old entering kindergarten without the need for support in school. Much like my daughter Lucy, some of these children are indistinguishable from peers and have lost the diagnosis altogether. I have never heard of a child becoming indistinguishable from peers when therapy is delayed to after four years of age. It is certainly possible that somewhere in the world it has occurred, but I have no knowledge of it. That being said, if starting later, using Gemiini along with the other therapies gives much better odds.

For older folks, Gemiini offers the ability to communicate more freely, or in many cases, communicate at all. It teaches social skills and life skills: everything from adult toileting to accepting disappointment calmly. Gemiini can improve articulation so much that people with Down syndrome who have adopted a habit of silence due to not being understood have become chatty and now feel confident enough to engage with strangers. People in their sixties or older who had suffered a stroke are regaining their voices. All of this is wonderful, and I don't want to downplay the importance of Discrete Video Modeling for older people, but, I can't emphasize enough the importance of starting as soon as possible.

Gemiini can't do it all alone. The daily video viewing sessions need to be reinforced with real-life interaction from therapists, teachers, parents, or siblings. Imagine if you learned a foreign language from video lessons, but never got to use the language. How much faster would you learn if people were engaging with you as you learned the new material? You would be able to build upon mastered words and concepts daily. Without generalization, or the live interaction of bringing the video content into practical use, don't expect to see meaningful gains with Gemiini—or any other therapy program for that matter.

* * *

Back when the twins were first diagnosed, I had no choice but to multi-task. It has become a way of life and twenty years later, I am still living by this philosophy. Little Luke, as the Gemiini community knows my youngest son, watches reading and Chinese videos on the drive to and from school.

Time management comes down to choices. By choosing to play "Teach Your Baby to Read" with Nicholas when he was an infant instead of watching TV, he advanced academically at an early age. This allowed him to focus on social skills as a teenager, which gave him the confidence he needed going into adulthood. The simple act of turning on the video camera attached to our TV during the twin's meal times allowed them to learn so fast that they caught up to their peers in language. By watching reading videos in the car instead of listening to music, Little Luke will overcome dyslexia by the time most dyslexic kids are just being diagnosed with it.

Time is our most precious resource and by far the scarcest. So much of our future is dependent on how we choose to spend our time now. These choices change the trajectory of our lives and our children's lives. The change may be imperceptible at first, but over the years it will be massive. If you only take away one thing from this book it should be this: No one ever regretted using their time wisely.

Chapter 17:
How Often And How Long?

I find that far too many parents have been told that there is no hope of independence for their child. This appears to be a pervasive problem in the UK, as comments like "Autism isn't treatable, you can only help the person to be more comfortable" are plentiful on Facebook from the British. These people evidently got this idea from their physicians. Maybe so few professionals outside the U.S. understand the potential of a person with autism because so few children with autism have had a robust therapy regime from the time they were two years old. They have never seen anyone overcome the dependence of autism, so they assume it isn't possible. This "factoid" is so entrenched that even famous success stories like Dr. Temple Grandin's can't seem to shake it.

Let me scream from the housetops, "It is not only possible for a person with autism to live an independent life, it is even probable, if one takes action early enough!" And the establishment that wishes to deny this fact, proven now by so many independent autistic adults, continues to cause great harm to individuals with autism and to the families who care for them. This is not to say that autism is "curable" per se—although my daughter, Lucy, would beg to differ, let me tell you— but that the autism diagnosis is not necessarily synonymous with lifelong dependence.

Yet, in many places around the world, people are told that their children will be dependent for life, not matter what the parents do. This creates parental despair and a resulting void of any kind of therapy. They believe, "If nothing will change, why bother putting in all of the effort?" One of the most compelling reasons for writing this book, and to highlight John in it, is simply to dispel this myth.

* * *

This point was driven home several years ago while traveling in Mexico. My husband and I were there to discuss a Gemiini Spanish website. John had offered to come along to watch Little Luke while we were in meetings. When the Mexican contingent learned that John was with us, they all wanted to meet him.

We called John at the hotel and told him that someone was coming to pick him and his brother up, and that he should use a certain code word to ensure he was getting in the right car. When I told our Mexican friend the plan over the phone, he sounded a bit confused. I found out later that he hung up the phone and said to his wife, "I am going to pick up an eighteen-year-old autistic young man and a three-year-old." His wife's first response was, "Who is watching them?" He replied, "I guess they are watching each other?"

I was surprised by their reaction, especially because they were familiar with our story. Despite all of the news, videos, and testimonials that everyone had seen about John and his recovery, the team in Mexico evidently didn't understand or believe that John functioned on a typical eighteen-year-old level (actually, he was much higher functioning than a typical eighteen-year-old boy, as I wouldn't entrust my three-year-old with any other!)

When our friends arrived at the hotel, they called up to the room and gave the code word. John put Luke in the stroller, brought down the car seat, and once again requested the code word before getting in the car. On the way to lunch, the hosts asked John about Gemiini, about his life now, and about his plans for the future.

When they arrived at the restaurant, our Mexican friends appeared to be in a state of shock. John took Luke outside to play on a playground, and our friends related the entire story to anyone who would listen. John really had overcome the dependence of autism. It was more than possible. They later told me that by meeting John, their expectations for their own autistic children had significantly increased.

The world needs to know John. It needs to know what is possible if the right actions are taken and are taken early enough.

One of the most frequently asked questions we get is "How long do we have to watch these videos?" The simple answer is, "Until the child is at least two years ahead academically and at age level socially."

I know that seems like overkill to most people, but it is prudent.

For typically developing people, most information is learned automatically, without our even knowing we are learning. Language, social cues, inference, cause and effect, and more all happen while we are just living. People with exceptionalities like autism or Down syndrome must be deliberate about their acquisition of knowledge. Learning takes longer and is more difficult to transact.

Our twins learned all of their academics at home, because the classroom offers many opportunities to learn beyond the curriculum. If the exceptional student must focus all his attention on academics, these opportunities are lost. Whereas a typical student might become bored and distracted if he is being taught something he knows, the exceptional student will be more likely to participate in discussion, and to pay attention to social cues and body language. Peers will also perceive this student as "the smart kid," which builds confidence.

I have seen comments from parents on social media that say something like this: "Gemiini is amazing! Our son used it for a few months last year and got his first words." This sort of message about short-term use is probably the most mystifying. Unless the child has miraculously passed up peers in a few months, there is just no good reason to stop using it.

The world of autism looks toward my John and Temple Grandin as a shining emblem of hope. I wrote this book to tell the world that John's progress didn't just happen. It took hours, weeks, months, and years of dedication and ingenuity. I have made it as easy as I possibly can for others by squeezing two decades of experience and success into Gemiini, but you still must actually use it to get results. Proper diet and nutritional needs are crucial. Most of all, you can't stop when the child is just "okay." A vivid example of this is a family who are Gemiini superstars:

> We began Gemini about 21 months ago. We have 2 children, both with autism. We had seen little results with the therapy we had tried to this point.
>
> At the time our daughter was 4 and she scored at the lowest 5% in receptive language. Our son was just 2 years old, he had only 15 sounds and almost no receptive language at all. He couldn't follow a single direction. Was very frustrated. No imitation skills at all. Very poor play skills too.
>
> Within a week of starting Gemiini, our son was pointing, imitating and saying all the animal sounds. By six months he was saying sentences. Now over a year later he is chatty and speaking in sentences all the time. He's just had a language test and he's ahead for age now! With the speech delay sorted he has become a social little boy and is just settling into his new mainstream preschool with ease.
>
> Our daughter first had small improvements in pronunciation, eye contact, attempts at conversation, watching people's mouth, and speaking more to a

person than to space. After another two months we noticed more improvements. She started to use some of the scripted conversations. After six months she had big gains. Last year's language score she reached 21%. After six months of Gemiini with receptive language score still in the lowest 10%. Fast forward another year and she's just had assessment last month and she's 47% She has caught up to her peers!

I feel Gemiini has allowed our girl to flourish in mainstream school. At start of primary she barely had enough words to enter the class. A year and half later she is top in her class for reading. Her receptive language is hugely improved. She's following directions. Expressive language is still challenging but much improved.

Additional achievements are a big increase in social behaviour. She is playing with children. Yes, she is still behind socially but she is definitely catching up.
I cannot recommend Gemiini highly enough. It has made such a difference to our children and their lives. It is so easy to use and relative to other therapies it is inexpensive. Due to the gains we have seen with Gemiini I now believe both my children will be capable of a successful independent life and that they themselves will determine their own outcome.

Thank you very very much!!

About six months after writing this message, the mother decided to take a break from Gemiini. The children were now so much improved that she felt she could "focus on other things."

The biggest fallout affected her daughter. As she had started Gemiini at four years old, she had further to go to catch up to peers. A year after stopping Gemiini therapy, her progress stalled in relation to those in her class, and her language use was again falling behind.

She was losing ground.

I do understand the temptation and thought processes that go into the decision to "take a break," as I fell for it myself once. When John was five, he had come so far that we lost our "first fervor" and stopped making weekly videos for a few months. The video creation was a huge burden on the entire family, and everyone just wanted a break. Also, John was starting to hate the videos. He would sit and eat and turn his head to the side, so he didn't have to watch them. He still learned everything and was scoring at over 90 percent mastery each week, so we didn't make a huge effort to make them more entertaining.

This is an issue that arises quite often with Gemiini members. With the increased access to just about any video ever made online, our kids are becoming video junkies and video snobs. Sometimes therapeutic videos can't compete for attention. The most important thing for parents to understand is that it doesn't matter. Your child may want to eat candy all day, but he won't be healthy if he does! Similarly, he may want to watch cartoons or some specific genre all day, but he won't be making language gains if he does. My best advice is to:

1. Edit the child's video to include more clips from our Humor section.
2. Upload your own short clips of things that the child likes, or of family members being silly, and add them to the child's videos. Keep these high interest clips to less than 15 seconds.
3. Watch during meals, car rides, and bath time.
4. Use a cord or Roku to play the videos from the tablet app to a TV screen and just let them play during the day. We find that even though the child doesn't look like he is paying attention, he really is, and a weekly receptive language tests will prove it.
5. Don't let them win! Once the child knows that this is here to stay, they will settle into watching and actually start to like it.

During the months that we stopped making videos, John made no progress at all. He was completely stuck, and was having behavior problems in therapy because he was bored. Once we started the videos again, he progressed as before, and we didn't make that mistake again.

The twins watched daily videos for over four years until they were nearly eight. After that, it was on an as-needed basis, because the themes were getting more complicated and we needed a bigger production budget. If I had had a tool like Gemiini, I wouldn't have stopped at all until high school or beyond, for some social skills.

The world around our children isn't "taking a break," and their peers are developing at breakneck speed—Every. Single. Day.

We as parents can't stop, because our kids can't wait.

This doesn't mean that the process never ends, but that it changes. We still use Gemiini in our home, but I use it more than John does. John will still do memory work on it occasionally (I wish he would do more.) When we have the interviewing and job skills videos up in the next year, he will watch those, as any other typically developing college grad should. I use Gemiini for sequential processing practice to enhance my memory as I age. I use the "upload your own clip" feature to memorize my lectures and to teach Little Luke his Chinese curriculum.

So many of the treatments for our children must be "all or nothing" to be effective. Gemiini isn't one of them. If you can only find five minutes one week, that's five minutes closer. You can make it up next week, or next month. It is true that the more children watch, the faster they will learn, but it is still teaching, no matter the frequency. So, if you have gotten a little behind, don't despair!

By using Gemiini's Language Pyramid as a model, parents can teach their children in any language in the world. It takes thirty to sixty minutes each week for these parents to film and upload their own video to the system, but they then have over twenty hours of language therapy to show their child. They can incorporate our x-ray clips to increase articulation gains. They can use our humor clips to increase attention. And, the app allows them to download their videos and take them on the go.

And best of all, their videos will always be there, and you don't have to worry about losing a computer. There is a step-by-step video on how to do this, called A Guide to Uploading Your Own Video Clips with Gemiini.

Just today I received a follow up email from the mother who "took a break" from Gemiini. She started back several weeks ago, and this is what she wrote: "Definitely seeing gains again already. She's partaking in a narrative group at intervention center and keeping up with them. Similar work last autumn was beyond her."

Gemiini isn't just speech therapy. It is life therapy, and the Johns and Temple Grandins of the world will never just happen while we "take a break."

Chapter 18:
What's In A Name?

There will, no doubt, be many people who take issue with my repeated use of the word *autistic* in this book. The battle between "person-first language" and "identity-first language" has been waging for decades, though in my experience, one side is fighting blind.

Person-first language teaches that we should not consider the label to be of more importance than the individual and that by labeling someone as "autistic," we are being prejudiced. This way of thinking says that we should all state that a person "has autism," rather than "is autistic." This is what all teachers are taught in continuing education classes and I found most have never even heard of Identity-first language.

Identity-first language teaches that the only reason one would take issue with a label is if there is something wrong with the label, and those who espouse identity-first language (typically, autistic people themselves) don't feel there is anything wrong with being autistic.

I must agree with the latter.

I, myself, was in special education when I was in elementary school, as was my husband. We were both in special classes for gifted students. I never felt the need to say that I "had giftedness," nor did my parents, nor my husband's parents. We were called "gifted" because there is nothing wrong with being gifted. By insinuating that the term "autistic" is a label that degrades, we do much more harm to the cause of neurodiversity than just about anything else I know.

Some of the greatest minds in the history of the world were and are autistic. I use the term proudly: I have seven children, a few are autistic, a few are gifted, a couple are dyslexic (which is another label that comes with great gifts), some are talented musically, some are athletic, etc. Labels don't scare me unless they are intrinsically evil. Those I will avoid, ignore, and try my hardest to eradicate. But, "autistic" is certainly not one of them.

In the end it comes up to personal preference and I don't ever correct anyone on this point. We all have the universal human desire to be accepted. That is one thing on which we can all agree, regardless of semantics.

Chapter 19:
Burning Down The Sewing
Machine Factory

Fear of change causes people do to bizarre things. A nineteenth-century innovator named Timonnier once patented a new machine that he had hoped would make army uniforms faster and better. When news got out, the traditional tailors of France feared for their livelihoods.

On the morning of January 20, 1831, two hundred tailors ransacked the new Timonnier sewing machine factory in Saint-Étienne. They destroyed the machines, threw the pieces out of the windows, and set the building on fire. The inventor fled for his life. Still, there was no stopping progress.

In 1961, Dorothy Vaughn was the supervisor for a team of women "computers" at the NASA headquarters in South Carolina. Using adding machines, these women worked in teams to solve calculations for the space program. When NASA brought in the first automated IBM computer, Ms. Vaughn saw that her team's jobs could be on the line. Instead of throwing the computer out the window (it was pretty heavy, after all), she became the department-wide expert on Fortran, the new computer language, and trained her team. NASA moved them to their new positions and gave them raises. They were now responsible for hundreds or even thousands of times more calculations. These women went from replaceable to indispensable.

In 2013, a group of distinguished behavior analysts presented a symposium on Gemiini to a standing-room-only crowd at CalABA, the California conference for BCBAs. Dr. Doug Moes functioned as moderator, and three Board-Certified Behavior Analysts presented findings in three separate studies. These studies were supported by videos of students, teachers, and therapists who had participated in the trials. The findings were exciting, and almost earth-shattering. After the symposium, a line formed out the door and down the hall to sign a request for the PowerPoint presentation.

Unbeknownst to the symposium observers, I sat in the back of the room and watched. I had never seen that kind of attention or interest in a BCBA conference. The room was packed, and positively electric. No one knew me by sight, and they didn't know that Gemiini was created by a mother who was not formally trained as a therapist. I stood outside the door and listened to people as they walked outside the conference. All the discussion had one theme:

"If this is so good, are we going to be out of a job?"

Hardly. If everyone in the U.S. were given the amount of speech or behavior therapy they truly needed to make optimal improvements, we would need over 5 million therapists. In reality, we have fewer than 150,000 speech pathologists and fewer than 50,000 behavior analysts.

We aren't even close to filling the need.

Each year, U.S. school districts battle to hire new speech and language pathologists (SLPs) to serve the ever-growing population of children with special needs. The demand is growing almost exponentially, despite the criteria for approval for speech services becoming more and more narrow. Talk to a speech pathologist who worked with children in the 1970s or before, and they will tell you they primarily worked on articulation. I knew an SLP who came out of retirement to help in the dire situation that many districts find themselves. She was shocked at the level of severity of her caseload. Another SLP told me that she goes home in tears from work because she knows that she could help her kiddos if she had more time with them, but with the thirty minutes per week that she is allotted, she just isn't getting anywhere.

Gemiini allows all the children in school to get the hours they need. It lets the districts treat the increasing caseload with their current staff. Children with articulation needs can be triaged to Gemiini in their pullout sessions, freeing up more in-vivo time for the severely affected children. It generates therapy homework that encourages and trains parents to participate more in their children's therapy routine. It also teaches non–English-speaking parents a common language with their own children as the videos are accessed by the entire family.

Jaymie Cutting, an SLP who has witnessed firsthand the difference Gemiini can make, writes:

Hi, I am a speech therapist in Clark County School District in Las Vegas. I paid for a Gemiini account out of my own pocket for a sweet 4-year-old student I service. He had been receiving 2 hours of ABA before school! (5am to 7am!!!), then he goes to an autism preschool program in the district where I provide 240 min. of speech therapy a week! And he was still making little to no progress! I was literally crying myself to sleep over this little guy. I stumbled upon Gemiini on FB and said, "What have I got to lose except $100?" So, it's been 2 weeks and he is spontaneously pointing, imitating the animal actions, and even some of the animal sounds! I'm beyond excited! I want this for every student! Our district needs this! Our kids need this! Thank you for this program! Thank you!

Jaymie Cutting, MA, CCC-SLP

Globally, the numbers for trained therapists are even bleaker. People in the UK will sometimes comment that they are fortunate, as they have health care paid for by their government. The reality is that children in the UK are lucky to get two hours of therapy a week, and unless they pay privately, no one is getting forty hours per week. In many areas of the world, including the United States, it is even worse. It needs to be made clear to all parents of autistic children that there is no research with live therapy—anywhere—that says that less than twenty-five hours of therapy per week can make a significant difference with a child with autism. Although anecdotal reports from our Gemiini community are saying that children are making significant improvements with just an hour per day of video viewing, these families are generalizing the video curriculum for several more hours each day and by doing so, distracting the child from the pull of his inner world.

A fully funded and operational forty-hour-per-week therapy program in the U.S. costs roughly $120,000 per year. This one child will completely monopolize the time of a therapist as well as take many hours per month away from several others. Leveraging time and money through the Gemiini platform, a therapist can now serve up to 260 students, with each of those students achieving greater gains, at a cost of a small fraction of the alternative. And this therapist can treat a child anywhere in the world.

Trained specialists' time can be leveraged another way: through time zone change. The afterschool hours of 3:00 to 7:00 are maxed out in nearly every city in the US. Allowing therapists to oversee clients in different time-zones opens up a huge pool of available therapists.

Lower-cost and more prevalent respite workers can take the place of highly trained specialists in places where there are no specialists. Specialists can now oversee large numbers of respite workers through teletherapy and reviewing a client's Gemiini account. This change must happen because the status quo is unacceptable.

Tell me, is it at all fair that a small fortunate few receive forty hours of therapy when so many get so little? And, considering this cost savings and greater efficacy, do you think that insurance will continue as status quo? Gemiini is in discussions with insurance companies even now. Automation is coming. For the good of the children, it must come. Those who embrace it will reap the benefits— both personally, as they will help so many more children, and professionally, as they will earn so much more money doing so. Those in the field who don't will end up like a CPA with a ten-key in a Microsoft Excel world.

Just today I received the kind of message that I am seeing more and more often. Marie Bacsik writes:

> I run a respite agency with over 600 families in San Diego. many of them pay much more out of pocket for speech therapy than the cost of Gemiini and speech therapy hasn't done much all these years. We have seen more success with Gemiini than with paying out of pocket for SLP... so we discontinued SLP and focus on Gemiini. I wanted to try it first with my own child before recommending it to them and I am sold now!

My heart sinks every time I read something like this, because I know how valuable a therapist's knowledge is when combined with the power of Gemiini. We see the fastest gains and the biggest miracles when the two work hand in hand. I wish I could sit down with every speech pathologist in the world and explain to them the opportunity they have, and the danger they face if they don't modernize. I want to partner with them. I want to offer training with Gemiini and be able to refer the thousands of parents who are searching for professional help with their Gemiini program. To prove my point, after Marie Bacsik read this chapter to approve her quote, this is what she wrote back:

> *Hi Laura,*
> *I didn't know you could combine Gemiini and speech therapy. I am EXTREMELY interested in learning more. I would love to help connect you with SLP's that are active in our community. Let me know what you think!*

Kids need twenty-five hours *at a minimum* of therapy per week. I am certainly not saying that I have all the answers, but with the brilliant people in this industry, no one has come up with a solution to serve this ever-increasing population. If they have and I missed it, I'm all ears.

Upon this writing, the designer Hubert de Givenchy has recently passed away. Would he have soared to the zenith of fashion without the sewing machine? Would Christian Dior or Ralph Lauren? Much like the early days of the fashion industry, we are striking out in a new era of therapy. Gemiini makes all this possible. The platform even allows therapists to brand and sell their own type of specialized technique. It allows for followers of these new techniques to be trained in the tens of thousands or even hundreds of thousands. It allows for children all over the world to experience the unique insights to complex situations that a therapist has developed. And it does all of this without the need of technical training or capital. All one needs is a login, a password, and a phone with a camera.

There are therapists who have already started down this road using Gemiini. Their practices are booming, and they are demanding higher fees than any therapists I know. They can charge per issue, rather than per hour. The parents pay less overall, but get more (for instance, just how much would you pay for your adult child to be toilet-trained?) The time has come where one can do very well by doing good—and do good for millions instead of just a few.

Who will be the icons of artistry in therapy in the years to come?

Chapter 20:
Can We Please Move On?

Initially, I had designed Gemiini to be a therapist's tool that would be used the same way it was used in our home. Therapists would create individualized sessions as therapy homework. I'd had so much success with parents at the autism conferences that I set out for the Council for Exceptional Children (CEC) conference with great hope.

Unfortunately, I couldn't get anyone to talk to me or even listen to what I had to offer. They looked at my card and said, "Are you a doctor?" or "What is your certification?" It became clear to me over the course of a few hours that there was a marked difference between parents seeking a solution and professionals hearing a pitch.

The cynic may say, "It isn't their kid," but I understand the distinction as something less sinister. With all the snake oil in the field of autism, professionals have seen so many fads come and go that they are weary of parents coming to them with the "treatment of the moment." They didn't know me, and my claims seemed outlandish. If I wanted to get the right people to talk to me at that conference, I realized, I needed to establish credibility in the next twelve hours.

I went back to my hotel and looked up the computer science department for Stanford University. I found the name of a new professor who was teaching human/computer interaction and called him. By the grace of God, he answered the phone and listened to my story. He said that he'd be interested in pursuing some sort of collaboration and would like to see how my trials progressed. He would also be happy to meet in the future.

I bought a pair of very low-powered reading glasses, put my long, blond hair up in a bun, and went back to the conference. This time when I introduced myself, I said, "Hello, I am working in collaboration with a Stanford professor for a scalable solution to therapy."

Every single person I approached with this preamble talked to me. They listened with true interest and attention. I was invited to the "insider" receptions and dinners. Most importantly, these professionals were now honest with me about their challenges and frustrations in the field of special education, and this information contributed significantly to Gemiini research objectives.

The obvious lack of a list of initials after my name has been an issue from the beginning. I find it interesting that the higher one is in the therapy world, the less one cares about the initials. Chairmen and department heads of universities, presidents of huge therapist organizations, and world-famous researchers never care nor ask about my education or accreditations. On the contrary, first-year therapists and special-education assistants are obsessed with them.

It is human nature to feel some sort of indignation when one has paid a lot of money and spent six or eight years learning something, only to have someone else come along who didn't spend the money do it better. I know that researchers on the Gemiini program have been attacked by their fellow BCBAs for daring to spend time researching a program that was created, as they have said, by "some random mom." With the success of the program and the seemingly limitless flood of testimonial videos and letters from parents, the focus on what is lacking after my name is definitely diminishing. But it still exists.

My answer to that righteous indignation is that dues are paid with different forms of currency. The SLPs, BCBAs, PsyDs of this world paid with money. The cost to me came much dearer, and it came in blood, sweat, and tears. Sometimes an education, in learning what has already been done, ends up limiting one's vision. Einstein is famously quoted for having said, "The only thing that interferes with my learning is my education." Dr. William Mobley, Chairman of the Department of Neurosciences for the University of Southern California at San Diego, told me, "I don't think you could have conceived of Gemiini had you been formally trained in special education."

I know I couldn't.

* * *

Every week we receive an email or a comment begging us to find a therapist who will oversee a child's Gemiini program. The market for this service is astronomical. Most people who go into special education are not mavens of finance. If they were, they would understand the massive financial opportunity that is possible through making their services globally available through the Gemiini platform.

We find that many therapists are just resistant to technology, in general, and not confident with it. Or, that they love Proloquo2Go or other apps that do not present a perceived risk of displacing them, but Gemiini is just too threatening. Some therapists have heard a lot of crazy rumors. Let's dispel some of them here:

Rumor Number One: "Gemiini is not evidence-based."

Video modeling has hundreds of studies published going back decades.[viii]

It is accepted as "Established" by the National Autism Standards Board and by every state or department of education in the U.S. Some will say, "We know that video modeling is evidence-based, but we aren't convinced about Gemiini specifically."

As video modeling has already been proven more effective than live modeling by Charlop-Christy in 2000,[ix] independent researchers did not feel compelled to study what was already proven. They, instead, chose research questions that would further the literature in meaningful ways. For this purpose, researchers chose to compare Gemiini's form of Discrete Video

Modeling to standard video modeling. This study was published by Portland State University's Dr. Maria Gilmour and found that Gemiini was over 300 percent more effective at achieving expressive speech than standard video modeling. It was published in the leading journal of technology in special education. [x] The second study also explored heretofore unanswered research questions on the utility of video modeling in articulation, reading, and advanced language acquisition. Its subjects were young adults, instead of the small children one typically sees in research of this kind. It was conducted by professors from three universities, including the former Director for Clinical Psychology at Princeton. It found that Gemiini was not only effective in these areas, but that the teachers were inclined to continue to use the program in school.[xi]

As of this writing, three more studies have been conducted, and two more are in the planning stages. The three in peer review are:

- The Effect of the Addition of Gemiini Video Modeling to Standard Practice in a School Setting: subject size, 160 students.
- Determining Best Practices in the Classroom for Discrete Video Modeling: subject size, 31 students.
- Comparing the Addition of Therapist Oversight to a Video Modeling Program for Students with Severe Apraxia: subject size, 31 students.

There are two more studies in the planning stages:

- A Randomized Controlled Trial Evaluating the Efficacy of the Gemiini Language Training Program for Minimally Verbal Children with Autism Spectrum Disorder (Helen Tager-Flusberg, Boston University and Pat Levitt, University of Southern California). This study will evaluate the neurological effect that Gemiini has through examination of the subjects using brain scanning as well as behavior.
- Evaluating the Effect of the Addition of Gemiini in an Early Intervention Scheme (Dr. Bryan Davey, BCBA-D).

To be clear, none of these studies currently in peer review or contemplated is necessary to establish the fact that Gemiini is evidence-based. They only serve to answer additional questions as to how best to use the program and why we are seeing the remarkable results, from a neurological point of view. BRIAN"S comment

Gemiini has received letters of support from therapists and doctors from around the world, but I think the following are two of the most impressive.

The first is from Dr. Bryan Davey, one of the most well-known and well-respected names in behavior science in the world. He is the CEO of a comprehensive clinic in Phoenix, Arizona, and President of the Association for Professional Behavior Analysts. Dr. Davey writes:

As the rates of autism skyrocket globally, traditional therapy methods struggle to keep up with demand.

Research conclusively reports that 25 hours per week of therapy is crucial to achieving optimal gains in early intervention, but few children are able to receive this benchmark due to multiple variables.

Decades of published peer reviewed research in video modeling show it to be an effective modality to bridge this gap in care. In fact, several studies point to video modeling being even more effective than live modeling in many areas. Gemiini is unique in the field of video modeling in its breadth of content, its delivery method and the research which supports it.

As the population of our autistic community ages, it is essential that curriculum and tools are created which are age and ability appropriate. Most technology or applications (apps) are geared specifically and solely for children 6 years old or younger. Gemiini's vast content library contemplates this older population and delivers robust curriculum through the teen years and beyond.

Many of our rural families have less than optimal Internet services, and others are facing financial challenges and thus do not have Internet at home at all. Gemiini's platform accounts for these potential obstacles by an app that allows the video content to be downloaded onto a device and used offline.

As Chief Executive Officer of Touchstone Health Services in Phoenix, we are seeing this gap in care due not only to the shortage of trainer professionals, but also to geographic constraints. Thousands of children and young adults in Arizona go without consistent services....We believe that the pairing of Gemiini with trained support is the way of the future and the best hope to serve the entire community.

Bryan Davey, PhD, BCBA-D, LBA
CEO Touchstone Behavior Services

The second endorsement comes from Helen Tager-Flusberg, PhD, a professor in the Department of Psychological and Brain Science at Boston University and the Departments of Anatomy and Neurobiology and Pediatrics at Boston University School of Medicine (BUSM). She is Director of the Center for Autism Research Excellence at Boston University and was President of the International Society for Autism Research (INSAR). She sits on the editorial boards of Autism and Autism Research, is an Associate Editor of the British Journal of Psychology and is Associate Editor for the Journal of Neuro-developmental Disorders. Ken Wexler, a professor of cognitive science at Massachusetts Institute of Technology (MIT), says of Dr. Tager-Flusberg: "If you asked somebody, 'Who are the famous people studying language in autism?' she's the first name to come to mind." Dr. Tager-Flusberg writes:

I am pleased to write this letter offering my support for the internet-based language intervention that has been developed by Gemiini Systems. This intervention is developmentally grounded and uses evidence-based practices, including video-modelling, repetition and imitation to promote spoken language skills in children and is especially useful for children with autism spectrum disorder. I am enthusiastic about how well Gemiini supplements more traditional speech and language therapies. It offers families the ability to practice and extend what their child may be receiving in just one hour a week of specialized therapy or, as is most often the case, provide high quality intervention when nothing else is available.

As a researcher who has been investigating language in autism spectrum disorder and related neurodevelopmental disorders for over 40 years, I am keenly aware of how crucial it is for children to have maximal opportunities to acquire language in the early years when their brains and minds are specially primed for this crucial developmental milestone. Gemiini can support this need. For those children who fail to acquire language in the preschool years, the methods that Gemiini uses helps older children to learn words and phrases that are so important for communicating their needs and interests.

In sum, I believe that Gemiini has developed a useful intervention for teaching productive language skills, an area of great need in the autism field, where there are no other comparable interventions available.

Helen Tager-Flusberg, PhD
Professor, Psychological & Brain Sciences
Director, Center for Autism Research Excellence
Boston University

Rumor Number 2: Gemiini is expensive, and having parents pay extra is not justifiable.

As we have covered, Gemiini saves tens, if not hundreds of thousands of dollars. A therapist's time costs between $50 and $250 per hour. And when that hour has passed, so has the therapy. At $98 per month for unlimited therapy, there is nothing more affordable than Gemiini in the world. Thirty minutes spent by a therapist creating a therapy regime for a client translates into dozens or even hundreds of hours of therapy after the therapist is gone. Using Gemiini between therapy sessions increases the rate at which the student learns, allowing parents to get a lot more "bang for their buck."

Adding Gemiini to a child's therapy schedule can reduce costs in the short term by reducing the amount of time needed for direct instruction. Whereas traditional modeling can take up to four hours per day, Gemiini can help individuals achieve mastery in only an hour per day. The live therapy time can then be entirely devoted to generalization. The long-term savings with Gemiini are extraordinary and incalculable. What is the cost to support an adult child with limited communication skills? What is the cost of respite or caregiving for life? What is the cost of worrying about what happens to this adult child after parents have passed on? What would I spend to give my child the chance to determine his own destiny?

Just as I am writing this book, my son John walked in from work. He told me he needed to borrow the printer for his new résumé, as he found a job online that really interested him. Would I have given $98 per month for a moment like this? Would another parent, if they knew a moment like this was possible for their child?

* * *

The Gemiini naysayers in the therapy community are a vocal minority. Many others believe them without investigation. This was illustrated for me at a recent autism conference. A speech pathologist overheard me speaking to the father of a boy who had used Gemiini with great success. The boy was now mainstreamed in kindergarten without aids and was on the road to losing his diagnosis. The therapist was intrigued, and she approached and said she was told by her colleagues that Gemiini wasn't evidence-based and that it couldn't be effective, no matter what parents were saying about it. She said that language was developed according to a hierarchy of skills and that teaching random words might produce little parrots, but it couldn't produce meaningful conversational skills.

I asked her if she had ever read the research on video modeling or the published research on Gemiini specifically. She was surprised to hear that there was published research. I asked her if she had ever actually seen the program. She hadn't. I told her that we were in complete agreement about the hierarchy of language development and asked if she had seen the Language Pyramid video. She hadn't.

I found a pair of headphones and asked her to sit down and watch the video. As she watched, I could see her nod her head in agreement. She then asked if she could see some sample videos. One by one, I pulled up videos that pertained to her requests. We had a video on every single subject she could think of. She was flabbergasted by the sheer amount of content and the way it was so easily arranged on the Gemiini website. She said it was nothing at all like she'd been told. She promised to tell all her clients about it and departed a Gemiini fan.

As a parent, if your therapist refuses to incorporate Gemiini into your child's therapy regime, ask him or her why. Be candid and be kind. Let them know that you value their wealth of experience and believe that their added expertise could greatly benefit your child. Ask them the following questions:

- Have you ever read the studies on video modeling in general?
- Have you read the published studies using Gemiini?
- Have you gone to the website and read the letters of support from professionals?
- Have you read or watched the testimonial letters and videos?

- Have you watched the Gemiini Language Pyramid video?
- Have you created an account and actually reviewed the videos?
- Have you ever used it with clients?

Anyone who answers these questions negatively quite simply does not have enough information from which to create an opinion. I haven't yet met anyone who can answer yes to these questions to hold a negative opinion of Gemiini. Jayne Higgins is a speech and language pathologist who has seen a sizable amount of speech fads come and go over the decades. When her own family was affected by autism, she chose Gemiini:

As a speech and language pathologist with over 30 years of experience, I knew what Gemiini was capable of the minute I saw it. I was fortunate in that I was introduced to it even before it launched to the public. This proved to be providential, as just after seeing Gemiini for the first time, my grand-nephew was diagnosed with autism. I had absolutely no reservations about getting him started on the program. In fact, I raced to Paso Robles to help to get him going. We noticed trouble with Brody at nine months: no babbling, no eye-contact, no comforting to mom and no joint attention. In Brody's early Gemiini days he would intermittently produce a sound (or noise) while watching the video and eating a meal. The progress was slow with no true word approximations in the beginning despite his age. He began to approximate more sounds as he watched the videos on a regular basis. Fast forward three years and this Easter Sunday he was telling family members that the Easter bunny broke into his house and explaining to his older cousin what color candy egg he wants. Brody is entering Kindergarten this fall WITHOUT AN IEP!

Jayne Higgins, MA, CCC-SLP

I have also found that my unvarnished honesty can sometimes come off as arrogance. Among my many short-comings, I talk too fast and can be blunt to the point of rudeness. I constantly feel the urgency of time, and I have very little tolerance for half-ass anything. I have made "insert foot in mouth" a new yoga pose. My faults, of which I am acutely aware despite my best efforts to rein in, could fill volumes.

Although I have precious little to boast of personally, Gemiini is another thing entirely. It is remarkable, and its success is documented. I know it works, and it works so well that I believe that every child with an exceptional learning style should be taught this way. I know that outcomes will improve with the addition of Gemiini even with the most accomplished therapist in the world. On this subject, I may appear to be arrogant. But it is the truth, and I would be a liar if I didn't plainly state so. ***Any therapy program, no matter the cost or the current results, will improve by adding Gemiini to*** *the regimen*. The fact remains that Gemiini works, and it has the power to reach the world.

In 2015, the owner of a large service provider in California received a call from a colleague. The colleague was very disturbed about some news:

Colleague: Have you heard about Gemiini?

Provider: No, what's that?

Colleague: It is this new online program and the testimonials are too good to be true. It is going to take our jobs. We have to all get to together to fight it!

Provider: What? I'm sorry, but no computer can replace me. If there is something new out there that is helping kids, then it is just another tool that I will add for the good of my clients. If you think you can be replaced by a computer program, you are in the wrong line of business.

A similar sentiment was reiterated by Dr. Amanda Adams at the California Autism Center when she was interviewed by ABC News about the prospects of Gemiini. She said, "Gemiini is a tool that should be in your toolbox along with good behavior intervention, a good school program and all that goes along with it. It is a supplement."

To put it plainly, if your child's therapist or school refuses to try Gemiini, despite the thousands of testimonials, published research, and endorsement from some of the world's most recognized researchers, there are two possible reasons:

1. *Ignorance of the aforementioned*– This is easily remedied by informing them. Once informed and the proof supplied to the therapist, it is my experience that most will embrace this new tool.

2. *Fear*– For the ones who still do not embrace it, if they have such little confidence in their own abilities that they fear a computer program will replace them, then as a parent myself, I would find a more competent therapist. My children's therapists could not have been replaced by Gemiini. It is true that Gemiini did replace most of the flash-card direct learning, but live therapy is so much more than flashcards.

From every point of view: financial, scalability, efficacy, and accessibility, Gemiini is the most realistic way to achieve the best outcomes.

Chapter 21:
Temple's Loving Push

I first met Dr. Temple Grandin in Los Angeles at one of her lectures. When John and I had the opportunity to speak to her privately, he immediately regaled her with a laundry list of his accomplishments, from learning language at four to college at sixteen. Her first question was, "Are you working?" His answer that he worked in the family business didn't impress her. She said, "You have to get a job outside the family."

I knew what she was getting at right away. Society tends to discount the ability of people who have had an autism diagnosis. Parents coddle their kids and want to protect them from bullying or ridicule. With the best intentions, many parents are ruining their children's chance at an independent life. Temple Grandin's book The Loving Push goes into detail about the steps parents should take to encourage independence and the mistakes to avoid.

For a parent who may be accustomed to doing everything for their child, letting go can be terrifying. In some ways it can be much more anxiety provoking than having a child who is dependent. For the sake of both the parent and the child, it is important to create a habit of self-sufficiency, and the earlier the better. Teaching a child with limited language to make their bed, clean their room, or do the dishes can be challenging. Gemiini's Life Skills videos take the pain out of the whole process. I know it might sound mundane, but very little in this world compares to the feeling when you walk into the kitchen to see your son loading the dishwasher.

About six months after I met Temple the first time, I was asked to present her with a lifetime achievement award in Birmingham, Alabama. I told the story on stage about her admonition to John and followed with John's reaction.

He went straight home after meeting Temple and got on Craigslist. He walked downtown and asked around at the local retail shops. Within a couple days, he had an offer of employment at a small grocery store. I have to say, when I heard about his responsibilities, I was a bit concerned. I know autistic PhDs who work in labs in universities who would have more difficulty doing John's new job than their own.

He was responsible for, well, everything. It is a small, independent store without "departments." John had to learn to stock the floor, work behind the deli counter, take food orders over the phone, deliver food on his bike, work the cash register, refill the coffee when needed, and keep the store clean. This transitioning from one task to another is something that is tough for most autistic people. Not for John! He moved from one thing to another with ease and, now, he even trains new employees. What can I say? Temple was right.

This experience transformed John in ways that I can't even begin to list. He is now independent in just about every way.

Chapter 22:
Healing the Wound With Love

It took many years, but I learned that just because I was capable of problem solving 24/7, doesn't mean I should. With a demanding global business and seven children who have their unique challenges (some of which dwarf the autism diagnosis), I could drive myself into the ground. Taking a mental break each day to exercise, read, and quietly talk to God improves mental clarity and is much more effective at relaxing than a glass or two of wine. The autism mom/wine connection is a running joke in our community, but there is a real danger of alcoholism.[xii] When the wine wears off, you haven't done anything more to help your mental state or your kids, and you will probably have forgotten any great ideas that you did have.

When something happens in one's life that, at the time, appears to be devastating, the first thoughts are typically, "Why me? Of all the people in the world, why did this happen to me?" I am not too proud to admit that this was the first thought in my mind when we received the autism diagnosis, and it lasted for several months. I have come to understand that these moments are all opportunities. They present the possibility of experiencing the joy of lifting a similar burden from others. And, by accepting our crosses with resignation (which doesn't mean passivity), they give us the gift of showing God how much we do love Him. He has done so much, including suffering a gruesome death, to show us how much He loves us.

That moment back in the autism conference, when hundreds of crying parents pressed me for help, changed not only my future path, but my perspective on suffering. If we help others by sharing the solutions to problems we have faced, then we turn those crosses into moments of joy. I can honestly say that autism is one of the greatest joys of my life: it has been the cross that carries me.

Our family lost everything in the mortgage crash of 2008. We lost our business and home, and our family was literally torn apart. Suddenly finding myself with so much time on my hands back then gave me the opportunity to travel to foreign lands to help others, and eventually, to found Gemiini. So, in a sense, abject poverty was the second-best thing that ever happened to me!

This "change of heart" has affected a lot more than just my perception of suffering. During this journey, my ideas of the concept of institutionalization have drastically changed. The word once terrified me, but a trip to Barcelona, Spain, let me see things in a different light. About an hour's drive from the city, there is a community of three stately mansions that were purchased to create homes for adults with autism. The residents have occupations and create artistic items that they sell. They have a garden, an indoor/outdoor pool, a gym, school, and cooking facilities. But, more powerful than all these amenities, is the sense camaraderie that the residents enjoy and which permeates all their activities.

Although technically an institution, this is a very, very happy place. The people who work here seem more like extended family than strangers thrown together: they have no worries, no cares, loads of friends, and a life full of love. Anyone in the world, no matter their level of independence, fame, fortune, or wealth, would envy their almost idyllic life.

As our autistic population is now aging, more residency homes such as this one should be created. We must start planning and building now, because if we wait until we need them, it will be too late. Many people who were thought to have low mental cognition are, in reality, locked inside their bodies, and in many cases, brilliant. We need to come together to invent if need be, careers for individuals who don't fit the typical mold of genius. Theirs is a unique form of intelligence that may require support in some areas, but that doesn't preclude a life of purpose.

It all comes down to perspective and the lens through which one sees the world is not fought against any outside foe. It is fought against my own procrastination, fatigue, prejudice, complacency and the status quo. At the end of his life, Saint Paul says that he had "fought the good fight," which is the perfect way I would explain not only my autism journey, but my parenting journey in general. I may have a few scars, but they are wounds of love that I joyfully earned by embracing the battle.

PART II

The following represents just a tiny portion of the fruits of our labor.

Professionals Sharing Their Joy

"As a speech and language pathologist with over 30 years of experience, I knew what Gemiini was capable of the minute I saw it. I was fortunate in that I was introduced to it even before it launched to the public. This proved to be providential, as just after seeing Gemiini for the first time, my grand-nephew was diagnosed with autism. I had absolutely no reservations about getting him started on the program. In fact, I raced to San Diego to help to get him going. We noticed trouble with Brody at nine months: no babbling, no eye-contact, no comforting to mom and no joint attention. In Brody's early Gemiini days he would intermittently produce a sound (or  noise) while watching the video and eating a meal. The progress was slow with no true word approximations in the beginning despite his age. He began to approximate more sounds as he watched the videos on a regular basis. Fast forward after three years of Gemiini, and early intervention from ABA, and this Easter Sunday he was telling family members that the Easter bunny broke into his house and explaining to his older cousin what color candy egg he wants. Brody is entering Kindergarten this fall WITHOUT AN IEP!"

- Jayne Higgins, MA, CCC-SLP

"Tonight I am over the moon about a 64 year old who had a massive stroke. He had lost all verbal ability, his wife was told he would never talk and had such brain damage he had no comprehension. Well tonight's session began with a Hello Margaret only prompted by me initiating a wave! He now can say many words and with ease as well as great articulation. He has gained power in his voice as well from all the repetition of Gemiini.

I use the receptive test to practice his receptive language and he scores now around 80% on several programs. Today I tested expressive and he really struggled but as I told him when we first started receptive he scored zero! I am filled with great hope and just wanted to share as I love this man and we are on a journey together! Thanks Gemiini!"

- Margaret M. (Speech Pathologist)

"I would just like to say I work with a individual who is 5 years old and has Down syndrome. He has been watching for half an hour, 3 times a day for about 2 months now and I can honestly say it's definitely helping. He talks a lot more and will at least say one 3-4 word sentence a day whereas before he barely spoke. And, when he did speak before Gemiini it was single words that wouldn't make sense. He enjoys the Gemiini program and sometimes will request it during his play time. I'm so happy this program exists and would recommend it. Thank you Gemiini!"

- Jess Rivera (Special Education Professional)

"We have been concentrating on just 3 words for a 14-year-old non-verbal boy, "home, bedroom, and potato chips" in Gemiini the past 6 weeks. These are high-interest words for him. He was watching up to 10 minutes twice a day until we increased his time yesterday. He was riding in the car with his parents and clearly wanted to go home and said "HOME!" The parents couldn't believe it! We can report that a non-verbal adolescent boy said a Gemiini word to get him where he wanted to go - this is amazing progress."

"Today I started Gemiini as a group in a class with 10 kids with autism. During the VERY FIRST video, one of the kids who has never said a word before in his life said "bear!" And he did the sign! I ran up to him and said "yes buddy! That's a bear!" He looked at me with the biggest smile ever and said again "bear!" Then, for the first time ever, he went up to a peer and gave a high 5. The teacher was stunned. I was in the class consulting for a few hours and our star student said "bear" 29 more times! I left the class before the second viewing but tomorrow morning I will return and I just can't wait to see the progress! This was IMMEDIATE acquisition upon viewing Gemiini. Even after two years of using Gemiini, these successes still bring me tears of joy!"

- Dr. Maria Gilmour, BCBA-D
| Portland State University

"Best news came yesterday! An 11-year-old non-verbal student I work with who has DS and Autism spoke his FIRST word yesterday!!!!! This past year he's been using PECS and for a couple of months now Gemiini. What I love about Gemiini is that he is now getting very focused on it, and when he watches, there's no stimming. Yesterday he said "Bye" twice as he was leaving! Loud and clear!!!! I AM SO PUMPED and so ready to go back in with my sleeves rolled up. Just when you think there's no change, he broke through! I hope this will inspire someone else."

- Anne C. (Educational Assistant)

"Hi, I am a speech therapist in Clark county school district in Las Vegas. I paid for a Gemiini account out of my own pocket for a sweet 4-year-old student I service. He had been receiving 2 hours of ABA tx before school!! (5am-7am!!!) Then he goes to an autism preschool program in the district where I provide

240 min of speech therapy a week! And he was making little to no progress! I was literally crying myself to sleep over this little guy. I stumbled upon Gemiini on FB and said, "what have I got to lose except $100?" So it's been 2 weeks and he is spontaneously pointing, imitating the animal actions, and even some animal sounds! I'm beyond excited! I want this for every student! Our district needs this! Our kids need this! Thank you for this program! Thank you!"

- Jaymie Cutting (Speech Pathologist)

"Where do I begin... First with a HUGE Thank you! I am a Special Education teacher of a classroom consisting of 5 male students (ages 5-7) with a diagnosis of Autism, DS, Cognitive Delays, and high trauma. I started using these Gemiini videos with my students about 3 weeks ago. The students are all reacting to it in different ways and it is enough to bring tears to one's eyes. The verbal students are repeating it to the non verbal students and the non verbal students are copying and now responding with words! At least 15 words now for one DS student who only had about 4 words before. My favourite today was the following directions in line. Today a student sat down for the first time when I asked without screaming! What I have learned as a teacher from these videos myself in these past 3 weeks. 1. I TALK too much!!! I mean I know the common saying "less talk" but was I really doing it? The answer to myself is No. I am still too talkative and wordy. After watching the videos with the students and then seeing them learn from them, all they need is the command (Walk, or sit, or stop screaming). Not, "oh, please stop yelling, that hurts my ears." I think all they were hearing was the last word ears). So today after the segment, "Lucy, stop screaming," the Assistant and myself had the opportunity to say to one of our students during an art project, "B stop screaming," and he looked at us with an aha moment and stopped screaming. It was a good day!"

- Jennifer Poag Guzman (Teacher)

"Two of my kiddos had been in the autism program here at school for 3 years and still didn't have any imitation at all, not even sound imitation. We started Gemiini in September and in the first week I noticed their mouths start to move along with the videos. By December they were imitating all sounds and words with everyone. By February they were speaking in complete sentences. When you find something that works it is so thrilling!"

- Alison Clark (Teacher)

Autism Triumph

"My son was completely non-verbal and 10 years old when we started Gemiini... Over 2 years later he said his first word and now (3 years) he can repeat almost anything! He's requesting & starting to use sentences! When I think about what we would have missed if we had quit too soon, it brings tears to my eyes. The only way to fail, is to stop using it."

- Hillary D. (Parent)

"My son is almost 6 with ASD and severe apraxia. He is nonverbal. We started Gemiini with him yesterday, just once a day. Today was the second time he saw the video....
He said elephant!"

- Sarah F. K. (Parent)

"We have speech!!! A combination of Gemiini every day, a diet change, multivitamins, probiotics, HBOT, MB12, and an intense little sister.... Liam has language! This was filmed on Sunday. Since then he has continued with copying words  with us and is starting to copy Gemiini on screen. So proud of him!"

- Dave Roper. (Parent)

"We began Gemiini about 21 months ago. Two children, both with ASD. Mentioned it to our ABA analyst who had seen early research and was very optimistic. We had seen little results with the therapy we had tried to this point.

At the time our daughter was four and she scored at the lowest 5% in receptive language. Our son was just two, he had only 15 sounds and almost no receptive language at all. He couldn't follow a single direction. Was very frustrated. No imitation skills at all. Very poor play skills too.

Within a week of starting Gemiini, our son was pointing, imitating and saying all the animal sounds. By six months he was saying sentences. Now over a year later he is chatty, speaking in sentences. He's had first language test and he's ahead for age now! With the speech delay sorted he has become a social little boy and is just settling into his new mainstream preschool with ease.

Our daughter first had small improvements in pronunciation, eye contact, attempts at conversation, watching people's mouth, and speaking more to a person than to space. After another two months we noticed more improvements. She started to use some of the scripted conversations. After six months she had big gains. Last year's language score she reached 21% after six months of Gemiini with receptive language score still in the lowest 10%. Fast forward another year and she's just had assessment last month and she's 47% She has caught up to her peers!

I feel Gemiini has allowed our girl to flourish in mainstream school. At start of primary she barely had enough words to enter the class. A year and half later she is top in her class for reading. Her receptive language is hugely improved. She's following directions. Still expressive language is challenging but much improved.

Additional achievements are a big increase in social behaviour. She is playing with children. Yes she is still behind socially but she is definitely catching up.

I cannot recommend Gemiini highly enough. It has made such a difference to our children and their lives. It is so easy to use and relative to other therapies it is inexpensive. Due to the gains we have seen with Gemiini I now believe both my children will be capable of a successful independent life and that they themselves will determine their own outcome."

- Liz L. (Parent)

"By the way, we did not make him watch Gemiini on the plane. He chose Gemiini on his own despite many other game apps on his iPad."

- Mariani D.L. (Parent)

"She said DOG!!! OMG!!! I thought I heard her say it through the first rotation of the video so when dog came around the second time I stood there and watched her. And she said it!!!! I watched her mouth to make sure I wasn't crazy and she really said it. I'm so happy I could cry! She even mouthed cat too just didn't say it out loud.

She is 4.5 with an ASD diagnosis. Also has global developmental delay. She is non-verbal. Only word she says regularly is "Go."

- Brooke N. (Parent)

"Two years ago, a friend sent me a link she saw on Facebook, and I scanned over it but put it in the back of my mind because it seemed too good to be true. I thought only "real" speech therapy would help. Finally, something told me to give it another look, and I had a different feeling...Hope! I figured we had nothing to lose. We are now almost a year in, and I've seen my 7-year-old previously non-verbal  son go from screeching as his default communication to attempting words first. He also has private speech therapy twice a week, but his therapist works with what he's learning through Gemiini to layer his therapy. We are witnessing a miracle."

- DeeDee S. (Parent)

"Stef was diagnosed with severe autism with Global development delay on the 6th June 2000. She did early intervention as per the practice of the time in Australia for 8 hours a week. She shared this early intervention with 9 other children and 6 out of the 10 remained non-verbal to this day.

Stef was enrolled at mainstream school in 2003. She was still not talking but she was listening and would follow simple directions. She had an aide at school 1:1 and they worked brilliantly together and her tolerance for crowds, new experiences and her interest in what other children were doing grew. She was learning her letters and her numbers and had about 15 words. Every now and again she would surprise us with a whole sentence. She then started duel placement at special school so that she could have the extra therapies. At mainstream school she was learning to add and subtract, but at special school they didn't even make her write her name on the top of her page.

At age 12, she was forced to go to special school full time and regressed to the point of no longer being able to write, do any simple maths or speak. There was a huge shortage of speech therapists both at the school and privately due to funding changes which meant under 6s had large amounts of funding and anyone over 6 got no help. We couldn't even buy a speech therapist, they simply were not available. The school relied on PECS and Proloquo2go as their only way of her communicating

At age 19, she was turned down by over 30 different speech therapists as they didn't feel that it was worth their time to try to help an older non-verbal person.

In May 2017 we started using Gemiini....Stef had about 4 words she used regularly... Not clear but we knew what they meant. Within a week of starting Gemiini, she had picked up 3 new words and said them clearly, after another week, 2 more. So now, 6 months later, she has about 40 words she can say...She has gained more eye contact, tries harder to participate in activities and with prompting is trying to say new words all the time. She is watching our mouths when we speak. We recently changed videos to words that are more ones which she can use in every day life. Foods, body parts etc. She is still shy about speaking... And rarely speaks to anyone unless she is particularly motivated (usually by food) but every word is an absolute gift and one step closer to being able to communicate her needs and wants to us all."

- Janine R. (Parent)

"I AM ECSTATIC!!!!!!!!!!!!!! We have had Gemiini for one month today but only really used it consistently for the last 2 weeks and Jacob just decided to show me that he can say the first 3 words in lesson 2.0!!!!!!!!!! Crab, Lizard, Bear---You have got to  be kidding me!!!!!!! So many happy tears!!!!!"

- Jenn V. (Parent)

"My son has been using the videos for a week now. We are at the very beginning of the program. However, he is low on the autism spectrum. Anyways I am so happy, he started imitating me when we were playing. He actually took turns playing and interact with me. It was like a dream come true. I am so excited to continue to work on this program with him. Thank you so much Gemiini!"

- Erin Q. (Parent)

"Teddie chose Colours and food for this evening's videos. The food videos show sign language as well as pictures. Teddie has started to copy some signs which is brilliant!"

- Parent

"We used Gemiini with each meal for 4 months before I heard any verbal attempt, but I wasn't worried! I had seen on Laura Live that she said to watch for better eye contact and him not being so spaced out all the time and we definitely saw that even the first month. He was also looking so intently at our mouths.

Then one day he just looked outside and said, "Dog!"

That was 3 years ago and he is now talking in sentences. He still isn't a chatterbox, but he CAN say whatever he wants to say (which is usually to complain or to eat, haha). In the past few weeks, he has just started to comment on things, which is amazing to hear. It is all snapping into place!"

- Ellie F.Parent

"We were told he would never talk. We used Gemiini with Alex for 1.5 years and it really worked for us. Alex started to speak after 4 months of using Gemiini and he showed a massive improvement in eye contact and receptive language from week one. Alex is no longer classed as non verbal and 90% of that I would say is due to us introducing Gemiini at a young age. Definitely worth it.

We are in the UK and stumbled across Gemiini in a desperate attempt to help our little boy. As I said, it worked wonders. My little boy also has Apraxia– hence why the speech did take a bit longer. In a classroom of his peers the professionals now have great difficulty even pointing him out as many of his ASD symptoms (traits etc) have reduced dramatically. Thank you for such a fantastic resource."

- Donna C. (Parent)

"Gemiini has been amazing tool for our son Colton. We can't say enough words to express the benefit from this program. He gets so excited to go to WalMart and it's not to buy a toy. Because of your program, Colton is excited to go to the produce department! That's right I said, produce department! He has

such excitement in his eyes and walks around with a big smile that would light up the room. He wants to show his parents what he knows. He will always find the broccoli first. He walks around smiling and sometimes jumping while identifying fruits and vegetables. He loves to put the items in our shopping cart. He is still a picky eater but, lately showing interest in trying a few new foods. The past two weeks Colton has started asking me, "What are you doing momma?" School has reported to me last week he is asking his aide, "What are you doing? Where are you going?"

He has learned about thunderstorms from this program and he loves thunderstorms! This program has taught him catch the ball and throw the ball. The list goes on and on. We put Gemiini in Colton's school last year. The program is amazing!"

- Dana M. (Parent)

"Gemiini video teletherapy did for our 3 year old in just a few weeks what months of live one-on-one therapy were not able to accomplish efficiently. No referral or diagnosis needed. We got a diagnosis months after she started the program and we believe Gemiini has truly helped us get the jump on treatment. We're starting pre-K this fall! That's not to say every child is the same, or every case is like  ours obviously... Parents need to look for what is working for their child. So very well worth the money - unbelievable results are literally "speaking for themselves" to coin a pun... Thank you from Debbie and me. This is truly a core part of our little one's treatment. Glory to God, and grateful for Gemiini!"

- Juan & Debbie P. (Parent)

"Just to encourage those of you who wonder why your child doesn't imitate the animals like the other success stories- we had NOTHING 4 months ago and now we are up to 15 different words a day being said up to 70 times. And this is just during therapy. He has gained 40 words/word approximations in the past 4 months."

- Jamie S. (Parent)

"We have two autistic sons 4 and 8. My 8 year old is doing well with verbal but our 4 year old is nonverbal. The Gemiini system concentrates on pronouncing words and the program repeats the word over and over and allows the child with autism to focus on the mouth not the whole face while pronouncing the word.

We have been doing the Gemiini program now for 4 weeks we have seen progress. Andrew our 4 year old has begun to mimic sounds which he did not do before, he is starting to mimic sound patterns during the session, plus our 8 year old now plays along during the sessions."

Dec 11th, 2015:
"Update our son has been doing the program 3 months. Increased mimicking of sounds. Trying to form words and said "Hi" today."

Feb 2016:
"Andrew said, "Bye" and waved!"

There are comments all over Gemiini Facebook by parents whose children start to say complete words the very first day, like this one from Todd Humphreys:

"This is an amazing program my son Liam has autism and in just three short months his vocabulary has gone from less than 10 words to around 100 words his understanding is through the roof and the progress is amazing. He also has speech dyspraxia so some of words aren't as clear as others but you know what he is saying. He has also started multi-syllable words too! I will recommend this to anyone I speak too that has a child with severe speech delays here in Australia.

Thank you, Gemiini,"

- James P. (Parent)

"Felix is 5 years old and had started saying one word at a time. For example, jump, come, mama, dada, etc. To indicate needs before we started Gemiini. Started Gemiini in May of this year. A week after starting, I took a video and was surprised that he could say the words on the flash cards. That gave me hope."

- Joycelyn D. (Parent)

"Started my 5 year old ASD daughter last week on Gemiini. She just started talking 6 months ago but mostly said single words like animals or foods that she wants. Her articulation is very poor. Yesterday I made a few new videos including the "I love you" clip. When I put her on the bus I told her "bye, have a good day at school." She quickly turned around waved and said "Bye, I love you mom." She's never said a sentence before. I was floored!!!! Thank you Gemiini!!!!!!!!

- Steph A. (Parent)

"When I took this video, it seemed like a miracle because he had never imitated before!! My son was 3 years + 3 months, and before that, the only sounds he had imitated were "mamamama" and "ba." That was the very first time

he watched Gemiini. Within a month, he was using 89 words spontaneously. In another two months, he was using hundreds of words and putting words together. Gemiini is what turned the key to unlock speech, after a year and a half of speech therapy had done nothing for him."

- Julia G. (Parent)

April 5th :

"I have to post because I'm starting to realize what a miracle this program is for my just turned 2 year old son with autism!

We started having him watch Gemiini about 3 weeks ago. He's had zero words until last week when he said, "g-f-sh" for goldfish! (I cried instantly!) Then yesterday while watching Gemiini at dinner and holding an apple, he looked at me pointedly, held up the apple (when it was on screen) and said, "aaaa-p". He completely made the connection...And wanted to show me!! (Both fish and apple are on videos we show him). It feels like a miracle is happening and we are so grateful! Thank you so much!"

April 6th:

"OK so now I totally credit Gemiini with being a miracle...I posted yesterday that my just 2 year old son with ASD had said g-f-fish for goldfish, but last night, he started doing so much more! He started saying, "osh" for ocean, "cuh-cuh" for cracker, "buh" for bear, "aaaa-puh" for apple, and "mom" ...all on command!!! I can't explain it but it is happening!! Thank you so much. We had thought he might be non-verbal forever so this is our miracle!"

- Amy B. (Parent)

"We started our Gemiini journey a little over a year ago. I originally joined to help my 10 ten year old son with Autism improve his clarity of speech, and increase his vocabulary. And although Gemiini delivered in both those areas, I am writing to praise the then unknown feature EYE TRACKING! This tool

is pure magic. My son, when reading aloud, would read so fast a sentence sounded like a very long unintelligible word. No matter what we did, his reading skills just stalled. About 5 months ago we started eye tracking (word by word) to force slowing him down. It instantly seemed to be the solution we were looking for! If slowing down and improving his reading skills wasn't enough, imagine our complete elation over EYE TRACKING also drastically improving his writing. Like his reading, his sentences were written without spaces in between his words--and we tried so many strategies to correct this! But low and behold, as he started to read word by word in eye tracking, he too began writing word by word. It took a few months, but the spacing just happened--He just began doing it!

Thank you Gemiini,

> - Gina P. (Parent)
> AKA: One thrilled Mommy"

"After 3 weeks on level 1. Interactive!!! Our son barely looks us in the eyes let alone now, pointing and grabbing for our attention! This made me cry. Watching the tongue and face video and then he wants to see if Daddy has the same while laughing! Oh my heart! This program is amazing & I am so excited to see where our son will be in 6 months!"

- Candice O. (Parent)

"We've had our son (just turned 5) in speech, occupational, developmental, and physical therapy since he was about 6 months old. We started Gemiini Friday night. Yesterday he said "cow" when his therapist asked him what the animal was, then he quacked when asked what a duck says. I'm in shock, I'm in awe, I'm in Heaven. I could kick myself for not starting this sooner, yet I'm so amazingly grateful that I found this.
Thank you, Gemiini!!!!!"

- Jamie W. (Parent)

"My son has been saying more and more words since he started Gemiini. The week after he started he went to school and they couldn't believe the difference he had made. Sometimes he doesn't seem interested in some of the videos but we keep playing them anyway. He loves taking the test after each one, he might not be paying attention to the video but soon as it's time to take the test he knows every single picture."

- Danni Dee (Parent)

"We first started, I believe, last January. I started off with putting it on QuickStart and doing the sessions as told. My boy took to them. He also loved home videos and YouTube video so this was up his alley.

We knew he knew the basics that Gemiini was teaching. At the beginning, he didn't say much and he still had that babble talk unless specifically asked about something and the occasional throw out of a word if really motivated.

Then I fell through with playing so much, even trying random videos so he wouldn't get too bored. Our child's main problem is speech and language as an ASD kid. I started playing them less and less. Why? Most of the time he would just turn them off himself. He didn't seem to be moving forward much and appointments took over.

I discovered a ps4 and TV connection this last month and started where I left off - randomly playing the animal ones and knowing where his language needed to go playing more advanced videos. Well, you know the "hi stop what's animal is this, stop, jump, stop, etc" video? I played it and he just started doing the motions and saying what was on the video. I taped it! I'm super happy with what I thought had no affect on my kid, except reinforce his knowledge and helping him say a few words he was already saying better. I went on to the animal videos and he was saying every animal sound, slow pronunciation with the faster pronunciation.

So I end with this Saturday night with Gemiini, this time I went to Conversation 1 beginning section - Saying "I love you, can you help me carry the box, are you hungry?" Well, it was time to go up for a snack and he went upstairs to my husband saying "are you hungry? "Today at supper, I said, "It's almost time to eat" and he sat at the table saying "are you hungry?" Which we are interpreting as "I am hungry."

Huge leap and bounds! Not only does he repeat these words, his pronunciation is much better and his babbling, (which we think is mimicking our faster-paced speech) has slowed down to a more understandable and more clear speech. And boy his requests are becoming more than 3 word requests/statements! He's now telling us with more assertiveness what he wants.

I will continue to use Gemiini as it has proven to be useful even when I thought my child wasn't listening. It's a tool for me – a mom who's learning to teach speech/language."

- Maria A. (Parent)

"We have used Gemiini with my 5 year old ASD son for a couple of months just to try it out. Being French speaking, we pretty much used most of the French content with him, a lot being about animals. We weren't on a specific schedule for the videos since we have other Therapies that keep him busy also. We just squeezed in the sessions when we could. During a trip to the toy store yesterday, our little guy ASKED (with sentences) to look at every single stuffed animal that he saw that corresponded to the words he learned in Gemiini. Last year, this kid had only a couple of words in his vocabulary. It's been over a month since we've used the program and still we are seeing results. He even uses the same accent as the person in the videos."

- Tina O. (Parent)

"Brilliant progress with my 2 year-old son, Grayson! Four words in the first month with lots of eye contact and interaction! He enjoys it too!

I was told that it probably wouldn't work especially as it's American words too. Well it proved them wrong... The speech therapist couldn't believe the difference in him these last 2 months."

- Carrieanne D. (Parent)

"So I caught my girlie pretending to be a Gemiini model this evening. She has come so very far - ASD, from severe speech apraxia, one word here and there to full sentences. We still have some work to do but couldn't have done in it without the help of Gemiini. Just listen to her enunciation. It takes time but for us it sure has worked alongside the other therapies we are utilizing. Thanks so much!!"

- Genevieve T. (Parent)

"Alex is 6 years old, he was diagnosed with ASD just after his 2nd birthday. He has some motor planning issues and apraxia of speech. When Alex was 4 we started Gemiini. We were doing good, he was attempting sounds he had never made before, fluoroscopy got him interested in his mouth and tongue and he would look in our mouths to see how we made words. We also saw eye contact increase, more awareness but speech is huge challenge so I knew we were in for a lot more work. No clear words in the 18 months of Gemiini.

Due to a change in childcare, we took a 3 month break. At the end of this summer, he went into a full imitation phase, whatever his brother was doing he would do. He took off on this bike like he always knew how to peddle, he started copying the way we sit, when we played "just dance" he joined in, playing Twister he joined in! I knew I had to start Gemiini and take advantage. This time I just did the [language] pyramid, and I am assigning canned videos and rotating them every week. We have animal sounds! The rooster, the tiger... the chick. He thinks is so funny when we all make like a chick. I also got his teacher interested, we are going to try to watch on this iPad in the classroom which will make it easier to get the 3 times a day repetition, since we can only usually manage 2 (breakfast with Dad and evening with Mom) That in a nutshell his out Gemiini story. Looking forward to next … however long it takes."

- Gina N. (Parent)

"When we started this journey a year ago, Jonah could say one word ("done.")

We had therapists work with him once a week, but once he turned 3, he graduated from that particular program and we lost all 1:1 support. Our evaluator told us that "early intervention was paramount in his development." We were on so many waiting lists (some over a year long) for any kind of help that we had to take Jonah's developmental growth into our own hands.

I saw an ad for Gemiini and decided to give it a shot. I didn't know if it would help or not, but it was about the only option we could find. It felt like if we didn't continue with his interventions, he would start to regress developmentally.

Gemiini ended up being a tremendous "first step" in our journey for us because it was something we could be proactive about. We could do it right from home or on any screen connected to the internet. And Jonah seemed to take to it as soon as we started.

The shapes and colors videos were some of his favorites, and here we are nearly a year later. You can see him applying what he has learned (foundationally through Gemiini, and now reinforced at preschool).

Seeing his learning go from watching it on the screen, to imitating the words, to understanding the correlation between concept and the word, to generalizing that knowledge outside of his learning environment--it is like watching a small miracle with every step."

- Jason (Parent)

"I have to share and hopefully will give others who are starting with Gemiini some hope... My son is 3 with ASD. He's been non-verbal and would only just randomly babble. No imitation, no echolalia, just vocal play and definitely no functional speech of any kind. We started Gemiini 4 months ago and he didn't say anything or imitate, but he started showing a huge increase in his interest in spoken language. I have been a Gemiini believer since the beginning because I saw the change in him, even though he wasn't speaking. Well, he just started pointing to letters and saying them. And today, this happened. I'm so happy and excited!!"

- Janette G. (Parent)

[On World Autism Awareness Day]

"SO.... Here's what's been happening in my house today to celebrate! What better way to celebrate with Joe talking more today than any day he's been here! We've heard "What does a Cheetah say?" "More bubbles!" To daddy when he stopped blowing them....

Shape identification
Joe: "Heart"....
Me: OMG Jason did you hear that?!?
Jason: no.

Me: Joe, what shape is this? It's a heart, can you say it again?
Joe: Heart (Jason beaming!)

Joe is outside splashing in puddles and counted all the way to 10 with every splash!!

We sing a song to Joe that he recognizes to get him to play on the bongos, I think we must of got at least 10 bongo solos today (chip off the old block!)

And to top it off he puts on a pair of dress-up glasses in front of the mirror ON HIS OWN!

So.... What's been happening in your house today?!? Happy happy happy World Autism Awareness Day. It's our first, and one I will never forget!!!!!!"

- Layla H. (Parent)

"We knew Cody especially would be slow to talk, but we could see how closely he paid attention to Gemiini. We knew it was getting through and we knew eventually it would come back out. Lainey benefited from seeing these videos from a very early age, because she would watch them with Cody during snack time. Once we realized she was probably on the spectrum too we were so thankful she'd been exposed to Gemiini all along. Thank you all so much for everything you do. Please know that what you do when you go to work everyday is making real differences in real peoples' lives!"

- Stacy V. T. (Parent)

"I have been doing Gemiini with my son, who was diagnosed nonverbal Autistic, for 4 months. He didn't respond immediately. I went into the Gemiini library and chose videos that said it would help spark verbal skills. I added those videos to his assignments. He is on a routine, morning Gemiini he views 4 times repetitively, then before bed 4 times, sometimes 3. But I take what He's learning and teach him sign language using the tools Gemiini taught him from the video. He started saying Yes, Thank you, & no, he will even sign those words. So I say to everyone who may not see results or is skeptical. I am an average person, mommy of 3, and this was the BEST learning tool I got for my son. THE KEY IS TO STICK WITH IT AND USE WHAT THE PROGRAM IS TEACHING THROUGHOUT YOUR CHILD'S DAILY ROUTINE. I hope this encourages someone, because I cried for weeks not knowing how to help my son. Now I cry because I can communicate with him, hear his voice with him actually communicating with me in "my world." So thank you Gemiini."

- Shanica H. (Parent)

"Just over 2 weeks into Gemiini with my son who is 29. He has learned to answer the question "Where are you?" appropriately from many rooms in the house. He now says "You're welcome" when someone thanks him and is **this** close with both "please" and "thank you" appropriately and not echoing. He is washing his hands much more thoroughly. His behavior has improved (less fixating on obsessions) because he has generalized "no repeating" for echolalia to his repetitive speech.

When we watch the videos together he has much better eye contact with me. AND...he does not like me touching him (except for tickling); if I put my hand on his leg or shoulder he always pushes it away....But NOW, watching videos, I'm "casually" touching him and he's not pushing me away!! And he is excited about all of these things---we finished a session and practicing a little while ago and he started telling me "Show Lynn (job coach) no repeating, please, thank you, wait in line, etc. etc!"

- Beverly F. (Parent)

"We started Gemiini in September when my son, who has autism, mainly spoke in 2 word sentences ("want drink"). Anything longer than that, the structure of his sentences made no sense at all (pragmatic language disorder). His receptive language was also really poor and most of the time he'd just say yes to everything I said because he didn't know any other way to respond. All this has changed with Gemiini, and last week my son who used to act like other kids didn't exist stood up in front of his class for show and tell and asked and answered everybody's questions for ten minutes with no support. I'm sharing this all over the place because I think everyone who has a disability or condition which effects speech development should try this."

- Kate S. (Parent)

"I cannot thank you enough for developing this program. After about 6 months of watching the videos, my grandson, Caleb, not only began repeating words, he signs like a champ! His frustration level has diminished greatly now that  his ability to communicate has increased. He counts to 20, knows his alphabet, recognizes foods at the grocery store... His Speech and ABA Therapists have recommended it to other Early Intervention families. Caleb's younger brother Gavin, who is being evaluated for ASD and receiving EI services, is also watching the videos. He just said his first word 2 weeks ago!! God Bless You!"

- Judy K.G. (Parent)

"My 6 year old without instruction watched for a bit, about 10 minutes in he started copying the close ups---articulating better, he folded his clothes first time ever because the boy in the video did, he washed his face and brushed his teeth and cleaned up after with no fight/issue (like the boy did), he used the word "almost" correctly on way to church "almost there"--like the boy reaching up could "almost reach", he had fun during the funny parts I added in (cowboy/ kids, cat videos, squirrel video, etc)....He watched a 20 minute video twice through (started with a boy saying his name on video---and he was sold! Lol) . I custom made it randomly last night after watching the tutorials. I have appointment scheduled for tomorrow. He is going to do great with this I am sure! We need help in expressive/articulation/conversation/daily life and school stuff. It's all there."

- Lisa C. Y. (Parent)

 "My 12 year old with autism has been completely non verbal his whole life, not even sound imitation. He did have 3 words for about 1 month when he was 17 months old, but "lost" those. Within 3-4 weeks of using Gemiini (he watches about 30-40 min a day total), he says 'pop' (for popcorn, one of his favorite foods) and 'bye' (not extremely clear, but it is there). He is also starting to form sounds/letters with his mouth (no voice, yet). It's a wonderful start for him! I've cried many days since we started about 6 weeks ago with the program. Tears of joy!

His SLP is very on board with Gemiini and uses it with him and several of her other clients now. We can't wait to see what the future holds! I would say definitely give it a try for about 6 months to see what happens. If my completely non verbal son can say some words after using Gemiini, I would say ANYONE can get some benefit from it. I wish he had quicker success, however, I keep telling myself that it takes babies 3-4 years to vocalize language, so I shouldn't expect 'quick results' from my son."

- Melissa L. (Parent)

"My grandson, Micah was non-verbal 3 months ago. Not one word. Very little eye contact. And I did not exist. After starting Gemiini, he has made leaps and bounds. Last night, for the first time in his 3 years, my grandson came to me to ask for help opening a box! He came to me, made eye contact, and said "Help." Best night of my life!"

- Karen H. (Grandmother)

"My son (29, intellectual disability, ASD, among other things) answered a WHY question this morning!!!! Ever since age 4 or 5 he would burst into laughter and we never, ever knew what he was thinking. I would always ask what was funny or why he was laughing and the best he might say would be "silly."

We've been walking the dogs/feeding the chickens each night and going over concepts from Gemiini during that time. Two nights ago the grass was wet and I asked "why?" and he responded with an answer that didn't make sense. So I said 'Look at the grass-- it is WET. WHY is it wet?" and he said "Rain." (We had a storm earlier). I was thrilled! But it gets better! This morning he was eating breakfast and breaks into laughter. I asked what was funny--why are you laughing? He said "You don't put jelly on your hat!" First time in 29 years I now know what made him laugh out of the blue! I immediately texted his job coach in excitement to share the news. It gets even better! Yesterday at lunch he was eating PB and J and got some jelly on his hat that he had to wipe off. So---he was remembering that, laughing about yesterday's memory, and TOLD me!!!!!! We've been watching the QuickStart "wh" questions for about 2 weeks now. Happiest mom today ever!"

- Beverly F. (Parent)

We started Gemiini when Aria was three, and had been diagnosed with ASD and non verbal. Gemiini opened the door for her to begin to try and speak. This was more effective for her than any speech therapy she attended, and we are so thankful we found this program!

- Kay Shumate (Parent)

We started Gemiini in February of 2016 with my son only being able to say some words and very short 2-3 word sentences at times which no one but me understood... by May of 2016 doing only Gemiini and diet change to GFCF he was having short conversations. Today he is a chatterbox!

- Sunny N King (Parent)

Mason began Gemiini in 2015 when he was 3 years old. At that time he was completely non-verbal and had been in speech therapy since age 2. Immediately upon watching the videos, I could see he was interested in watching. Shortly after, he began studying my mouth when I spoke and even started reaching out to touch my mouth. I knew something was clicking in him. I kept on with Gemiini every day for 4 months until he finally said his first word – "Apple" at the supermarket (while grabbing an apple). It was amazing! From then on, we have continued with Gemiini and his language has SOARED! He is now 6 years old and can read and spell and type words into a computer. We've also used Gemiini for tons of behavior modeling and also to expose him to things like birthdays and holidays. It works wonders and I'm so glad Gemiini found its way into our lives!

- Janette Gaunt (parent)

Gemiini showed up on my Facebook feed at the perfect time. I was a panicked mom looking for help while we were on therapy waiting lists. Our little guy had very simplistic speech, just enough to get his needs met. The minute we started, his speech took off and it wasn't just imitating. Now our 18-month-old who shows signs of autism watches them with his brother. Nothing is sweeter then hearing a little voice say "iPad, Gemiini please"

- Leni Jensen Crow (parent)

How it began....

One night feeling desperate and defeated I looked up at the stars and asked my Dad to please help me get through to my 2 beautiful babies who can't speak to me. Both with autism and 1 with severe apraxia. They were 3 at the time. As I was scrolling through Facebook I suddenly stopped when I saw the word Gemiini knowing it's twins and knowing my father was a Gemini.

I saw Laura Kasbar speaking of her twins and how it changed her life and I knew this was my sign from my Dad above to try it.

Well the first time I put it on Mia my daughter started saying "Bear" then she went onto "Cassowary" and after that she repeated everything including the whole skit from "What does a bear say" etc... my son Leonardo took longer but he is 5 now and asks us "What does a lion say" etc...! We haven't stopped exploring with Gemiini and we won't stop. It's been a daily tool in our lives and we are so grateful for it. The first picture is the twins watching Gemiini together.

- Kimberly Fusca (parent)

Down Syndrome Success

"We advanced levels in Gemiini... Level 5...Putting a sentence together with using yes and no questions. He knows NO very well. He understands YES and says it when prompted, but typically when I ask him a YES question, he responds with confirmation of my last word. For example "Do you want applesauce?" He'd reply "sauce". I'm so excited to see how we make this transition! If you haven't signed your kiddo up yet...I highly recommend you do."

- Christie L. (Parent)

My son Christopher has Down syndrome. He is at a combiner word stage. His clarity drops when he uses more words in his sentences.

My husband and I have used Gemiini for the past week.

Tonight Christopher started reciting the song "family finger"; daddy finger where are you... He said the entire song so clear, I literally stood back in shock! Delighted this programme is having such an effect with him!

- Eileen C. (Parent)

"The day before my birthday in March, Olivia spontaneously said, 'I love you mommy' -- TWICE. I think I died. It was at that point that I knew I found something amazing for my child... For any child with a speech delay, really. I highly recommend you check it out."

- Christine H. (Parent)

"I have people ask me all the time how Lily's speech exploded. I have referred so many people to Gemiini because it is working! What is so interesting to me is that she is saying things that are not even in the videos now. It's like something clicked for her!"

"I am SO excited to post this video. Last week I saw a video on Instagram showing a child with Down syndrome learning through the Gemiini system. I was intrigued and signed up for a free trial week. Lily has only been using these videos for a few days and we are already seeing huge progress in her speech. She has always struggled to add the ending sounds to words – but notice in this video she very clearly says FOOD and CUP with the ending sound. She has also struggled to pronounce words that start with F, so the fact that she is saying FOOD properly is huge evidence that this learning program is already working. Sam and I are so anxious to see what Lily's speech is like in the months ahead, if this is the result we are seeing after just a few days of lessons. We have also heard her say words the past few days that we've never heard her use before .. and asking for things using sentences. Rather than her traditional "la la la Cheerios" she is saying "I want Cheerios, please" without any prompting!"

- Patti R. (Parent)

"I cannot emphasize enough how he does not talk.. I see posts from people talking about their 'non verbal ' kids and then go in to say how many words they can say or repeat. Nathaniel has NEVER said anything.. No d, b, l, p,.. nothing EXCEPT a "mmm" sound when really prompted (and it takes some prompting)! In just a week he literally said, "no" as clear as day in response to his dad asking him for a cuddle! He's not repeated it and in fact shakes his head in defiance when  he thinks we want him to talk! He's a little monkey lol. He'll be three in April. This week, since starting Gemiini, he's humming loads whilst playing and signing. And really tries to 'moo' because that's what a cow says lol! He'll go 'mmmmmm' trying really hard. When he wants to! Thank you!"

- Maggie I. (Parent)

"I am sure you have been receiving a lot of testimonials from parents lately about how amazing Gemiini has been for their child/student, and I would like to add to that. We started in January with our daughter Naomi, who will be 3 on April 21st and has Down syndrome. I had read a few positive comments here and there about the program on FB and decided to take the plunge- with no financial commitment I felt we really had nothing to lose. And since then we have done nothing but gained!!! It is so obvious that connections are being made in her brain because she is like a different child. She had barely any words when we started, and now my most recent count is over 70 words... which I know does not include all of them, it's just what came to mind when I tried to do a quick count the other day. But it's not just words... it's answering questions (still simple yes and no questions, but a few months ago she couldn't do that), it's counting from 1 to 10, it's calling for our attention (particularly her big brother who she is obsessed with!), it's requesting (food, toys, etc), it's saying "please" and "thank you." It's so many things. I am so excited for her to start preschool in September and blow her teachers away with all that she knows and is capable of! We do a lot of traditional therapy (4 sessions of speech a week, 3 PT and 3 OT, plus she goes to a special needs toddler school) but I know it's Gemiini that is helping those connections form, so that what she is learning through her other therapies can be maximized! We haven't even made it through 1.0 to 6.0 yet (we jumped around in the beginning and only a few weeks ago decided to commit to doing the program "right" so we started back at 1.0) and if we have seen so much progress already, I can't imagine what is yet to come. Articulation has and will continue to be a huge issue with Naomi due to her low tone (she has incredibly low tone, even for a child with DS) but I know if we keep using Gemiini she will only get better. Thank you for releasing this before it was perfected- I will take it, technical issues and all (although we have had very minimal technical issues). And thank you for always being available on FB to answer questions and help parents, therapists and teachers out. My next goal is to get her speech therapists and then her preschool teachers on board!!! Thank you from the bottom of our hearts for helping our daughter as she continues to grow, mature and change perceptions of what children with DS are capable of!!!"

- Corinne E. (Parent)

"We've been using the program for a couple of months. My son (who has Down Syndrome) was very communicative, but not very verbal. I'd say within the first couple of days, he was imitating the words in the videos. Within a week or two, he went from being primarily non-verbal, to primarily verbal. He mostly uses single words to label or request things, but we're getting some two word combos as well "Bye, Mom", "Ella, come", etc."

- Sarah F. K. (Parent)

"First time. He's enamored. Is this system hypnotic or something? He had just brought his favorite movie, Star Wars, to the table. This is very unlike him. — Feeling hopeful."

- Mary S. (Parent)

"We started the program [Gemiini] a week ago. I'm super impressed. This is Emry – he's 13 months with Down syndrome. In just one week, his understanding has improved dramatically!"

An update on Emry's progress:

"Poke and kisses are on his video. He is learning sign with each new word. Ball was in a video a few weeks ago."

- Rachel L. (Parent)

"Just wanted to share a story. My son with Down syndrome has been trying to jump for a long time. We have tried everything! We have tried the trampoline, pool, peer modeling... We have been watching the 6.0 video this week. Yesterday, while outside, we were practicing following the directions like stop, run, sit down... I said jump. He jumped! I clapped and was very excited! He started clapping and he said, "I ump mama!" Whoopie!!!!!!! I at that point started crying!!!"

- Kelsey M. (Parent)

"Sometimes we practice speech and potty training simultaneously. Aside from "bye" these are all new words! Words she didn't know a few weeks ago before we started Gemiini. I am amazed and in love with this program. I told her teachers and therapists when I started the program so they could also see if they noticed a difference, all of them tell me how her speech has exploded! It's not just the words in the videos, she is trying all words and looking at my mouth for guidance. Speech has always been our biggest setback and I am thrilled beyond words with Gemiini! Thank you Instagram moms for introducing it to me. And isn't her "cheetah" seriously the cutest thing ever?"

- Catherine B. (Parent)

"Big news y'all! When you've been working so hard using Gemiini for nearly a year and your almost 8-year-old non-verbal child FINALLY starts using her voice!! She was TELLING me, "A bite," or, "more," each time she wanted another bite and saying, "Mmmm yummy," and then said, "Ahh done," for all done! Then she 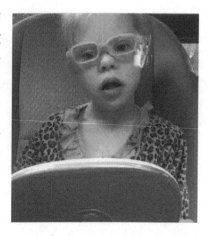 said hi to the bus driver and told me bye! My heart is so full! She has the sweetest voice I've ever heard!"

- Corrina J. (Parent)

 "We had three breakthroughs today! She made the sound of a bear, moved her tongue like a lizard and attempted to say "lizard". I have seen a tremendous increase in her chatter, as well. I don't know that every day will give us huge results, but I'm so excited about her progress so far!"

- Courtney B. (Parent)

"My 4 year old son with DS goes to school twice a week. This week when I picked him up his teacher said she's seen a big improvement in his language. She asked me if we are doing something new. Um wow! Yes! Gemiini! And we've only been doing it for two weeks and I feel like we aren't even doing it exactly like we are supposed to! So now I'm really studying it to make sure we are doing it right and as often as possible because it obviously works for us. Very excited!"

- Mary Beth T. (Parent)

"Today she's said: White, Pink, Purple, Orange, Green, Dove, Yellow, Black, Blue, and Gray, SHE'S DOING IT, Y'ALL!!! If you know someone who is nonverbal, please let them know about Gemiini! Don't ever give up on those sweet babies!!! OH, and she's FEEDING HERSELF!!! No big deal!! Aaaaand I'm secretly bawling on the couch with the biggest smile on my face!!"

- Corrina B. (Parent)

"I love the power of Gemiini. I have been feeling like Reese is glued to her electronics and playing with toys less. So I created a custom session of just kids playing (see preschool games category). One of the videos shows a group of kids playing with PlayDoh. After watching 1 time this morning, she immediately went over to the toy closet and pulled out her PlayDoh set. We set it up and she played for about 30 minutes."

- Jennifer B. (Parent)

"I am a mother of a 6 year old who has Down syndrome. We were so lucky to have been using Gemiini for approx. 2 months with our son. His reading and articulation have improved dramatically in that short amount of time and we can't wait to see where he goes with this! What's so amazing is that we can understand what he's saying!! He was very hard to understand but with the articulation tools on Gemiini we are amazed with the results. The program is easy to use and it is very effective for kids with Down syndrome who are visual learners like our son. We couldn't be more pleased!"

- Ingrid T. (Parent)

 "Success in action! L.... is 12 years old with Down Syndrome and has been doing advanced vocabulary with Gemiini for a few weeks. Her teachers have already asked her about word choice in classroom writing. "Wow, L.... 'Abrasive' is a great word! So is 'reluctantly'." L.... wants to write a book – that's been her wish since she was little. "Juicy words" empower her to further believe she can be an author."

- Jane W. (Parent)

"My daughter is 21 with DS. She had reached a point where she would just look at me every time someone spoke to her. She knew they couldn't understand her. One month with Gemiini and we are seeing eye contact and voluntary greetings! She used to just parrot back the last thing we

said when given a choice. Now she at least tries to say what she really wants. Gemiini is one of the best things we ever did for her I highly recommend it!!!"

- Betty B. (Parent)

My son Will now 5.5 –been using Gemiini since before age 2– speaks in complete sentences, asks questions, uses adjectives, narrates his play, is understood by strangers.

- Dani Viscomi Verro

Unknown or Multiple Diagnoses

"In the past two days, my grandson Logan, for the first time, pet a dog. It was an actual stroke of the fur from head to hinney, twice. He also held and hugged, for a couple of minutes, a stuffed animal. He is 2 years 9 months old. This is huge. He has been using Gemiini since November. He continues to be without words but his social interaction and eye contact has improved immensely."

- Connie P. (Grandparent)

 "Here's Jacob deciding which lesson he wants to work on today! We have been using Gemiini since August... It's the best decision we've made so far for his speech... And he loves it!"

- Jenny V. (Parent)

"At age 6, Gemiini gave my beautiful boy his first words! Here he is only 7 months later reading aloud. My heart is happy, light and heavy at the same time! Keep up the fight and most importantly the hope moms and dads!!"

- Brandee B. (Parent)

"My daughter is almost completely typical and talking now! We do some little conversational things with Gemiini and I tell people about it every chance I get. It was a godsend I thank you very, very much for developing this. I was at my lowest point and crying every day when I found Gemiini and with it came hope that I had some control over the situation and every day we could work on it with her. Maybe I couldn't pay for that speech therapist or drive the hour and a half to a bigger city to a speech therapist but I had Gemiini right in my home!! I had great support and help over the phone if I needed it from all the people who work there. We are going to keep our membership probably at least for another year, even though I don't even have a job but I have it on auto pay and we try our best to remember to get it paid for and so we really appreciate it. It has changed my life in the direction toward success, success and more success so thank you very much from the bottom of my heart."

- Patricia Q. (Parent)

"I'm truly grateful for Gemiini. A friend suggested trying Gemiini almost a year ago but I was concerned about finances.

I wish I hadn't waited.

Our daughter has made big improvements communicating and is trying harder to speak in longer, complete sentences. I smiled to myself the other day when another child attempted to take a toy from her and she responded with, "Hey, don't take that. That is mine, it is not yours." In the past she'd just yell, "No!"

- Janice G. (Parent)

"I started Gemiini about 3 months ago. It was the first thing I tried when my then 17-month-old was labeled "at risk" for autism. We have been watching the animal sounds videos repeatedly and I've even made some of my own. Just this past week, my son started talking. He only says a few words (car, mama, dada, pawpaw, kitty, uh-oh, juice) but he knows so many animal sounds. I had no clue he was absorbing all of those. He knows elephant, sheep, monkey, snake, dog, cat, tiger, and lion. It's really incredible. His speech therapist is amazed! He is picking up more animal sounds every day. I have to admit, I was skeptical but not anymore. Thank you Gemiini!"

- Megan S. (Parent)

"We started Gemiini at the beginning of August and we are halfway through the 7.0 lesson. Yesterday my 2-year-old non-verbal son woke up from his nap, sat up in bed, waved, and said "hi" like they do in the video! Love it!"

- Jennifer L. (Parent)

"Just wanted to say that I have been using Gemiini for about a year now and it has helped my Son hugely. He has between 50 - 200 word labels under his belt but still doesn't tend to put sentences together. Picking the right videos could be a bit overwhelming with the previous Gemiini and I just want to say thank you so much for this new update! It is amazing and I feel so much more confident that I will be using the correct videos for my Son moving forward. As always, thank you to Laura Kasbar for creating this therapy for our children with extra needs. And if anyone is reading this and wondering whether to try Gemiini, I would say go for it!"

- Natassia M. (Parent)

"I just wanted to say thank you, I somehow found Iris Grace's page which brought me here and I just took a leap of faith and decided I had nothing to lose to try this program.

My son Z has just turned 3 in November and I have been trying just about everything to get him to talk. He has just about zero clear words (other than "mommy, and no") and he is undiagnosed with anything. He is extremely bright, it's if he moves too fast, his mind is so busy he can't slow down enough to get words out. When he does they are incorrect, as if he has articulation problems. Example I'll say "Dino" he'll say "diyou".

He has been going to school for his early childhood program for three months now and though his behavior has gotten better (following directions) his words haven't seemed to change. He has been doing speech therapy every two weeks since he was two.

I started your program two days ago, first day he was actually trying to say fish and we watched for an hour after school during his dinner time. Second day, again after school during his dinner. He said bear and lizard almost clearly...I almost cried. I can't wait to see how he is progressing a month from now. I'm so excited.

This is Z watching and holding up his elephant picture that he sorted out of the pile of animals himself."

- Sahra C. (Parent)

"My son is 5 in just a couple of weeks and also almost totally nonverbal. We have been using this program for a few weeks now and I am so impressed with it. We are seeing gains that have seriously taken almost a year to accomplish with regular speech therapy. I am so thankful for this program. Try it! You have to give it a shot. I was pretty skeptical but decided to give it one month. I am so glad I did!"

- Heidi R. (Parent)

"My son spoke more yesterday during speech therapy than he ever has. We have been doing this program for almost 3 weeks. He has been going to speech therapy for 5 months. We are so impressed with this program and become more and more hopeful everyday."

- Natassia M. (Parent)

"My daughter used Gemiini for just a few times and very sporadically throughout a months time. I chose assignments that Laura suggested, Focusing on tools for mental and motor connection. All the sudden she's reading words and I almost can't keep up with her. Something in her just connected. She's learned to read about 60 new words in the last few weeks alone. This is huge improvement!"

- Mj D. (Parent)

"This is the day after!! So happy with Gemiini and my Boo Thang is lovin' it!!"

- Meeka N. (Parent)

"I live paycheck to paycheck. I applied for a scholarship and got approved. There are different qualifications for the scholarships too that can help out. After I tried it, I can't even put a price on my son's progress. It really works and he loves it! Better than anything else we've ever tried!"

- Adri M. (Parent)

"JJ started using Gemiini for the second time 6 months ago. During that six months he has gone from a vocabulary of 20 words when prompted to over 100 words with independent short sentences. His growth has been so great that his teacher is now integrating Gemiini into her program at school for JJ and the rest of her class. Raising a child with special needs really does take a village and we would like to thank Gemiini for being an integral part of our son's village."

- Jacob B. (Parent)

"At the mall, after watching the Gemiini cowboy video, my daughter just climbed onto the moving toys then asked for 'coins' to put in and she stayed on it for 3 rounds!! She used to hate things like that before."

- Georgie V. (Parent)

"I would like to say that this program is the best thing that has happened to my family. My son who was non verbal in any way is now saying up to 25+ words. Today we were watching dog videos on YouTube and he said 'dog' and proceeded to make sounds like a dog. I teared up with joy. I am beyond happy that I took the leap of faith and clicked on the 'more info' tab on Facebook. This has been an amazing journey."

- Clorina H. (Parent)

"The Gemiini App brought enormous fun to standstill traffic on the M25: listening and joining in with my passenger and budding communicator Sam."

- Cheri H. (Parent)

"I have 2 children on the spectrum and Gemiini has been crucial in my children's development. "

- Parent

I have been doing Gemiini for 4 months and had not seen the results that others have seen. I was about to give up (in tears writing this), but I read a comment from a parent who said that she had a call with the Gemiini staff and it made all of the difference.

I couldn't live with myself knowing that I might have been doing things wrong, so I signed up for a call and IT DID MAKE ALL THE DIFFERENCE! I made the adjustments that Gemiini recommended and HE SAID HIS FIRST WORD!!! Not only that, he is loving it now, whereas before he would scream. I didn't know about the "hater" sessions (my son is definitely a hater, at least he was.) Now that we have found these he runs from the other side of the house to watch! I am so hopeful!

Thank you so much Laura for not giving up on the ones that are picky like my son. I can't believe I almost quit! I may have never heard his little voice.

- Brenda K. (Parent)

"Discovering Gemiini was the moment I finally felt like I had some control over how I can help my son. Prior to that I spent hours and hours laminating PECS cards and trying to make it all work any way I could... And that has certainly all helped too. I felt like it was in Gemiini, though, that I found a tool that he loves that makes me feel in control. It was like watching his brain light up and make connections about language. If you sign up and it's not working you can request extra help with strategies. It's not a magic fix of course! We've got years of working on his language ahead of us but I absolutely believe that Gemiini has (and still is) really helping him to connect the dots.

"I didn't need any further proof that Gemiini was awesome but it keeps coming... This morning I asked Max (age 7, primarily only verbal for scripting and requests) if he had finished his breakfast and got no answer. This generally means yes so I took his plate and his milk and started walking away with them. He quickly said, 'I have none!' Which is a quote from one of the Gemiini videos that demonstrates sharing and quantities etc.

In the video the boy/girl says, 'I have none!' and then the other child gives them some back. So it was Max's way of telling me he wasn't finished! It's a brilliant example of how scripts become their language! Max has also been known to use movie quotes and song lines as language too. These kids are amazing!"

"Max was watching his Gemiini video about hamburgers so I asked him if he would like a cheeseburger. He said yes! So I bought him one and he pretended to eat it and studied it and opened it and nibbled on a tiny edge of the bread. This is HUGE for him! I'm guessing a couple more attempts and he will actually bite one!"

- Cheri H. (Parent)

Laura,

Thanks for the quick response! We are sooooooo excited to be using this system. I have HOPE for Garrett's language and reading future like I've never had before. Just today he said "Mom, Ethan Elijah my house today?" His two best friends... He was wanting them to come over. The amount of COMPLETE sentences...Just sentences more than 1 or 2 words is amazing!!! My husband and I are laughing because he is also brushing his teeth an AWFUL lots these days as well as taking a shower and wrapping himself in a towel when he's done. It's just WONDERFUL!

I also want to let you know that as soon as I read over your payment policy and ALL the options you have available, most importantly your commitment to leaving no child out because of financial restrictions...I was IN! I have been incredulous over the years of these specialists who have "all the information and magical solutions" for our kids...But we will go broke using them. It is incredibly upsetting. Such a gift that you make this possible for other kids.

Have a great night!

- Jenny (Parent)

"E... has been doing absolutely wonderfully with your program. It is like something is clicking in his mind to make all that has been absorbed just roll right out. The "I Love You's", the pointing and saying "I want that", and I ask, "And what is that?" and he will make an attempt to sound out the word. ...The best part because the communication has increased gigantically; he is less aggressive with his behavior...This past week my husband and I have shed many tears of joy. You have saved my son and will, always be very grateful!"

- Jessica P. (Parent)

"My little Abby asked to watch the sports video I made on Gemiini! She kept saying 'base a ball,' 'base a ball!' I finally figured out what she wanted! Thank you Gemiini for making this wonderful program available! Hearing my baby girls sweet voice is so amazing!"

- Brenda H (Parent)

"Wow. Just God knows my regret now for quitting and losing 2 years of Gemiini. My daughter is putting her videos by herself and she is choosing her favorites and saying everything! I sit with her and we start mimicking but today she surprised me; She told me about one of the videos and said, "Look she's attacking him with the flower!!!" I'm still in shock and I cried of happiness! I highly recommend any parent here to give it a try and don't think a lot about the money because you will have your own SLP at home and kids start loving the videos and program. I'm very happy with the results in just a week using Gemiini again."

Elivert V. (Parent)

"My son started Gemiini almost 2 months ago and he is starting to say a few words! The other day he said a complete sentence, "I did it!" I was so happy I almost cried! This has given me so much hope, so glad we decided to give it a try."

-Melissa A. (Parent)

"Using the potty training video for 3 days now with my 5 year old non verbal and he has successfully gone pee 2 mornings in a row now!! Dad and I have been working hard at potty training and we are now seeing results after 2 days of watching the video!! Sooooo happy with the results I am seeing from my son and this program I wish I would have started last year!"

- Kirsti L. (Parent)

"I love how my little boy, aged 4, has begun to modify the scripts from the videos to make sense in his daily play & daily interactions. His latest special interest is airplanes, and on the way home from school today he said, "What am I? A plane! What sound does a plane make? Whooooooooosh!!"

Earlier this week, he wanted to request something to eat. He said, "Ooooh! I'm hungry! Do you want banana bread or orange juice?" (These were the choices available to him at the time) " I want orange juice. Thank you! You're welcome!!"

I believe in gestalt language learning! I can't wait until he begins to customize and recombine even more!

Gemiini is giving me the gift of seeing how bright my little guy really is, and giving me even greater hope for the future. Who cares that he scripts sometimes?!? Don't we all? Better to be functional at scripting and practicing sequencing longer sentences than getting frustrated not knowing how to say what's in your head (my little guy has apraxia of speech too!) I feel Gemiini supports traditional SLP gains all the way.
Bless you Laura Kasbar and family!"

- Kimberly V. (Parent)

"Any skepticism I had about Gemiini is gone!! I just heard my son say "What does a Bear say?" Clear as a bell!! Hand gestures and everything! He's only been on the program for two weeks and I'm soooooo encouraged! I never think I could be any prouder than I am and then he surprises me and does something else previously unthought-of. He works so hard. Who knew growing up a three year old would be my biggest inspiration?"

- Parent

"Last night I learned about Gemiini, this morning I joined the program, tonight my 4 year old was trying to say words while watching. The interaction he had with the Sessions was phenomenal. My wife and I can't believe it! The very first try at it and we see THE LIGHT THAT HE WILL FOR SURE SPEAK!! This is amazing. Thank you So Much...
Jeannot, Susan, and our son, Donavan."

- Jeannot S. (Parent)

"I'm so very impressed with this program! This evening my daughter and I were eating candies that made our tongues turn color and she turned to me and says "can you explain why your tongue is blue?" So I replied and asked her the same question (except hers was red) and she giggles and says "cause my candy was red silly"! Thank you from the bottom of my heart. Not only is she understanding but she's generalizing it!
Best money I have spent in a very long time!"

- Sherri R. (Parent)

"Sean started just saying the last part of everyday "day", after 2 views he was saying all the days with no problem! I love this program, he learns so much more in few sessions, than in school everyday!"

- Elizabeth C. (Parent)

"I'm so excited! We have been using Gemiini for under a week and I have seen amazing improvement in my 3-year-old! I know that sounds crazy, but I'm watching this unfold before my eyes! Here's an example: He has struggled with the word "fix" for so long. He usually says, "seek." He could make all the individual sounds, he just couldn't put them together. Out of the blue today, he clear as day said, "fix."His articulation has significantly improved in just six days. I tell everyone who will listen about Gemiini!"

- Nancy B. (Parent)

"Around age 4 her first word was "medicine" though we never heard it again. By age six she had nearly 40 words. Then we started Gemiini. Now she has hundreds of words and is consistently speaking in 3-4 word sentences. The words she has, she truly has, not here today and gone tomorrow.

All this to say, though it is hard, don't get discouraged, while it took us years to get started that little snowflake we pushed around for what felt like forever finally formed a ball and now it's starting to roll downhill faster and bigger everyday."

- Elizabeth G. (Parent)

"It's happening! My son just came up to me and said "up!" Because he wanted me to get up and come with him. This is the first time he's said up, instead of uh, and the first time he's ever said anything independently, without prompting. I am so proud of him, and so excited. We just started Gemiini 6 days ago!"

- Sarah M. (Parent)

"OK just have to post. We have been using Gemiini for maybe 2 and 1/2 weeks and my verbal but non-communicative son age 5. He is starting to communicate!......

Not exactly like the videos but he now says water if he is thirsty. And we were watching the food labeling sessions I set up and they were on apple and he said "chicken." I said, "no, apple." He said "chicken" again and went to the refrigerator and got out a piece of leftover chicken, wagged it at me and said, "chicken!" (haha)

He also said "I love you" to me this morning! ...

2 weeks ago occasionally he would ask for water....Maybe 1 or 2 times a week but nothing else and no responses to questions. And tonight he got up out of bed and I told him go back to bed and he said, "go potty." !!!(He is potty trained but has never asked to go to the potty....I just have to show him where a bathroom is so he can go when he needs to and if we are in

public and I don't take him, he would never ask, just eventually have an accident if I didn't take him. So this has been amazing!!!)"

- April D. (Parent)

"Decided to give the Gemiini a try. We heard about it from a few different places, and I figured it can't hurt so let's give it a shot! Started over the weekend and Lia is loving it so far. Attempting to make the sounds she is hearing, has learned a few new signs, and is very interested in the videos. It's A LOT of repetition, but I knew that would be no problem for Lia as she loves watching the same shows over and over again anyway. Excited to see what adding this to our home therapy will do for her."

- Kelly (Parent)

March 21th :
"My son Zach was thrown from a car 6 years ago. He had frontal lobe, multiple shearing and tearing, anoxic, and brain stem damage. He has been non verbal, but we know his vocal cords work because he has cried out in pain before.

He is using Gemiini, a learning program originally created for kids with autism, to help Zach relearn how to talk. It is going to be played for him 2 to three times a day and we will first see if we can get "mom". and then we shall be using several different videos and as he progresses. Please pray this will help him."

March 30th:
We just started the program a week ago. However the other day he said "MOM" as clear as a bell in front of a nurse and myself! I was so proud and told him so and he was grinning from ear to ear. As was I and the nurse.

Our motto is STAY STRONG ZACH KEEP THE FAITH. Right now he likes me to play "yes", "no" "want", "hurt", and "mom." Praying for more to come!"

- D S Smith Johnston (Parent)

 "I have two daughters ages 4 and 5. My 5 year old has Down syndrome, ASD and apraxia. My 4 year old has high functioning ASD. I am very excited to start using the videos with my 5 year old, who is essentially non verbal. We watched the first video tonight and she didn't want to turn it off!! Also, she tried to make the 'Bear' sounds!!"

- Kristina L. (Parent)

"We've almost completed our first day with the program. And I've been wiping away happy tears for most of it. My 2-year-old son is mostly non-verbal, (his only functional word is bye-bye), has sensory processing disorder, and we are waiting for our autism evaluation. He did 3 (count em 3!!!!!) Imitations today. I can't believe it! What a wonderful day!"

- Emily C. (Parent)

"We got "bubbles" clear as day! 5 months in with Gemiini and we customized a session to enhance his speech therapists target of getting him to say the sound "b". We had bubbles, bus, blue, banana etc. First run through and he says bubbles. This is huge for us. Alex is only 34 months and has apraxia and language delay, SPD and suspected ASD and is classes as non verbal. Gemiini has helped massively with his receptive language and understanding and we knew we needed to stick with it to see the benefit with his expressive language and it is worth every second. The thing is, Alex doesn't always like watching the sessions so they are played at random times and it often looks like he's not even watching. Yes I have been known to follow him from room to room holding the iPad in his sight because meal times do not work for us. But everyone has noticed the difference in him. Yes I cried and I'm sooo proud of him. Had to share because I see some parents losing hope after a few weeks. Hopefully Alex's progress will give them hope."

- - - - - - - - -

"My little guy is also 3 in July with apraxia. We are 5 months in and we have words now. They are not always clear but they are consistent and used in context. He says mammy, daddy, grandma, bubbles, ball, bear, no and he will also  now try to say words when requested by his therapist. She is ecstatic with his progress x forgot to add- he now babbles non stop and at Christmas was completely non- verbal."

"It took about 6 months for words to start and I can't express how fantastic it is to hear Alex call me Mummy now. He gets it right every time now. We have lots of other speech like words and he recognizes shapes, colours, some letters and the numbers 1-10 as well now. Was sitting at the traffic light today and when they changed to green he shouted out `geen es go` (green means go). Not perfect I know, but I'm taking that as a sentence and we all did a happy dance and proceeded to shout it out at every traffic light we went past on green."

- Donna C. (Parent)

"Ceris (Rhymes with Paris) is 8 and has Down Syndrome, CAS, a protruding tongue, hypotonia, and Autism. She has had ST, OT, and PT since she was a baby. She has had swallow studies, sleep studies, and she is currently scheduled for another swallow study. We have done home therapy, gone to specialists outside of the home for ST/OT/PT as well. We've tried the preschool prep, abcmouse.com, we've tried where you put her hand on our throats to feel the vibrations. She's never been interested.

Then we heard about Gemiini, and have been using it since September of 2015. We were about to cancel it in July of 2016 because she just wasn't interested in it. We were broken. When we really didn't have anywhere else to turn, we realized that Ceris is just a late bloomer. For example, even with all the therapies, she didn't even start walking until she was 3 1/2.

So Gemiini was the only thing she was any sort of interested in. So we started picking up the pieces. Although she is still not at a conversational place yet, she will get there, and we have Gemiini to thank for that. I'm so glad we didn't give up.

Honestly, I cannot express how heartbreaking it is to tell my daughter I love her and she not say it back. She now says, "Hi" to everyone she knows. She says "bye-bye" she literally started waving last week. She is not potty trained, but she says "pee-pee" when she wants to go potty. She can say lion, fish, monkey & makes the ooh-ohh ahh-ahh monkey sound. She can say green, purple, blue. She can say rectangle, triangle. She can SING her ABC's and she can COUNT to TEN!

 Although she doesn't say, "I love you" yet, she says "Nite-nite" since using Gemiini, she follows instructions more, such as paying attention when we are at the store, or wherever and she will stay in line at school. She stays in her seat more at school, and she is more attentive in general. She used to be mostly in her own little world, but now things are just starting to 'click' with her. We are unbelievably grateful for Gemiini.

They say having a child with special needs is like taking the scenic route. You still get to where you are going. It may take a little longer, but it will be well worth the trip. And Ceris is an amazing tour guide. I stated earlier that we were broken. Well, Gemiini has truly been a piece we've been missing. As you know, progress is progress, no matter how slow you go. Gemiini has helped us become whole, and Ceris will be very verbal with time and practice (and lots of patience & faith)."

- Corrina B. (Parent)

Acknowledgements

With heart-felt gratitude to my family for lightening the load and to all the Gemiini team for their incredible service to the community. Thanks to Elisabeth Spaeth, Inland Imaging, David Coombs, Bill Murphy, David Black, Debbie Shepherd, Thorsten Larsen, Kelly Greyson and family, and to Pamela Phillips, the one person in the world who pushes me harder than I push myself.

Notes

[i] O. Ivar Lovaas, "Behavioral Treatment and Normal Educational and Intellectual Functioning in Young Autistic Children," *Journal of Consulting and Clinical Psychology* 55, no. 1 (1987): 3–9, http://www.beca-aba.com/articles-and-forms/lovaas-1987.pdf.

[ii] Deepa Bharath, "Most Influential 2014: Laura Kasbar," Orange County Register (December 24, 2014), https://www.ocregister.com/2014/12/24/most-influential-2014-laura-kasbar/.

[iii] Nicholas Carr, "The Web Shatters Focus, Rewires Brains," Wired (May 24, 2010), https://www.wired.com/2010/05/ff-nicholas-carr/.

[iv] Kok Suen Cheng and Ray P.S. Han, Poh Foong Lee, "Neurophysiological study on the effect of various short durations of deep breathing: a randomized controlled trial," Respiratory Physiology & Neurobiology, pp. , 2017, ISSN 15699048, http://ieeexplore.ieee.org/document/7292237/?reload=true.

[v] Christopher Lee Keown, Patricia Shih, Aarti Nair, Nick Peterson, Mark Edward Mulvey, and Ralph Axel Müller, "Local Functional Overconnectivity in Posterior Brain Regions Is Associated with Symptom Severity in Autism Spectrum Disorders," Cell Reports 5, no. 3 (2013): 567–72.

[vi] Larissa Morlock, Jennifer L. Reynolds, Sycarah Fisher, Ronald J. Comer, "Video Modeling and Word Identification in Adolescents with Autism Spectrum Disorder," Child Language Teaching and Therapy 31, no. 1 (2015): http://journals.sagepub.com/doi/abs/10.1177/0265659013517573.

[vii] Dulcie Lee, "MPs Urge Action on Lengthy Wait for Autism Diagnosis," The Guardian (October 15, 2017), https://www.theguardian.com/society/2017/oct/14/autism-diagnosis-waiting-times-jeremy-hunt.

[viii] Scott Bellini and Jennifer Akullian, "A Meta-Analysis of Video Modeling and Video Self-Modeling Interventions for Children and Adolescents with Autism Spectrum Disorders," Exceptional Children 73, no. 3 (Spring 2007): 264, http://journals.sagepub.com/doi/abs/10.1177/001440290707300301.

[ix] M.H. Charlop-Christy, L. Le, and K.A. Freeman, "A Comparison of Video Modeling with In Vivo Modeling for Teaching Children with Autism," Journal of Autism and Developmental Disorders 30, no. 6 (December 2000): 537-52, https://www.ncbi.nlm.nih.gov/pubmed/11261466.

[x] Maria Gilmour, "Comparing the Teaching Efficacy of Two Video Modeling Programs Delivered in a Group Format in Special Education Classrooms to Improve Expressive Language," Journal of Special Education Technology 30, no. 2 (2015), http://journals.sagepub.com/doi/abs/10.1177/0162643415617377.

[xi] Larissa Morlock, Jennifer L. Reynolds, Sycarah Fisher, Ronald J. Comer, "Video Modeling and Word Identification in Adolescents with Autism Spectrum Disorder," Child Language Teaching and Therapy 31, no. 1 (2015): http://journals.sagepub.com/doi/abs/10.1177/0265659013517573.

[xii] Jackie Olson, "The Alcohol Solution for Mothers of Autistic Children," The Fix (September 29, 2015), https://www.thefix.com/autism-moms-and-alcohol-self-medicating-after-diagnosis.